Early Literacy Assessment and Toolbox

First Edition

Edited by Michael S. Mott, Jacqueline M. Mott, Susan S. McClelland, Lisa H. Thomas, Angela S. Rutherford, Katie Y. Naron, and Jerilou J. Moore

University of Mississippi

Bassim Hamadeh, CEO and Publisher
Michael Simpson, Vice President of Acquisitions
Jamie Giganti, Senior Managing Editor
Miguel Macias, Graphic Designer
Jennifer Allen, Acquisitions Editor
Sean Adams, Project Editor
Luiz Ferreira, Senior Licensing Specialist
Kat Ragudos, Interior Designer

First published in the United States of America in 2016 by Cognella, Inc.

Cover image copyright © Depositphotos/gbh007.

Printed in the United States of America

ISBN: 978-1-63487-983-5 (pbk) / 978-1-63487-984-2 (br)

cognella®
academic publishing

www.cognella.com   800-200-3908

CONTENTS

SECTION III: TOOLBOX FOR TEACHING USING ASSESSMENT RESULTS

INTRODUCTION

WHO SHOULD USE THIS BOOK, AND HOW SHOULD THEY USE IT?

Early Literacy Assessment and Toolbox is a book for teachers, teacher education students, and reading specialists for assessing and teaching critically important skills involved in the reading process to K–3 and students with exceptionalities. This book is an invaluable supplement to your existing comprehensive reading program. Using a simple process of asking questions based on included examples, or "items" from the assessment, a teacher can record results to understand what level of competency a student demonstrates. Results enable the teacher to learn about important reading skills in need of teaching and reinforcement. Educators and researchers have identified two key areas or skills that enable effective reading to take place. The first skill is sound discrimination, which is referred to as phonological awareness. The second skill is the ability to understand parts of words—such as *un*, *re*, *intro*, and *ed*—that function to change the verb tense or part of speech (meaning) of that word. Knowing word parts, or morphemes, and having morphological awareness is important for enabling the reader to understand the meaning of a given word.

Most importantly, this book can be used to maximally increase your students' ability to learn to read by strengthening student existing reading skills for increased reading comprehension. Recent research in education has revealed the following:

- Sound assessment and games/activities: Phonological awareness (PA) is vital to making the sound-symbol connections required of phonics.
- Word part assessment and games/activities: Morphological awareness (MA) leads to an increase in vocabulary as the understanding of word parts—such as *dis*, *re*, *ant*, and *poly*—provides access to understanding the larger word.

A key ingredient contributing to literacy achievement is awareness of sound units and word parts. Classroom teachers can use this book with individual and small groups of students, with the assessment and corresponding five- to fifteen-minute-long learning modules/reading games, to address key reading subskills of PA and MA. Reading specialists can use this book to address reading difficulty issues students have that can be ameliorated with a focus on PA and MA. It is important to note as well that the easy-to-use assessment and learning modules can be used by parent volunteers, student teachers, and teacher aides.

ASSESSMENT AND TEACHING OF PHONOLOGICAL AND MORPHOLOGICAL AWARENESS FOR READING ACHIEVEMENT

ELA contains two parts, sound assessment and word parts assessment, with subskill sections for each part. The assessment is easily administered by a teacher, assistant teacher, or adult volunteer and merely requires that you read the directions, review the practice item with the student, and then proceed to read the one-line questions (or items) to the student, who in turn responds. The student answers questions you read line for line to the best of his or her ability, and you record correct/incorrect using the answer in bold embedded for you in each section of the assessment.

Throughout the school year it is recommended that you assess your students intermittently (every other month) to determine which reading skills you should focus on for their instruction, and this process should be used to complement your comprehensive reading program already in place. Other reading areas of phonics, fluency, vocabulary, and comprehension are positively impacted by assessing and teaching sound assessment and word parts assessment. Differentiation in reading instruction is not always easy to accomplish, and using the ELA results to point you to the exact corresponding learning module/reading game (or "mini lesson") will support you in teaching directly in the area of student reading-skill need.

TEACHER IMPLEMENTATION

The ELA is simply an assessment, for both sound and words, that comes with a toolbox for teaching exactly where the student needs instruction. Here is a walk-through of how this works in the form of an example. Our student is "Lucy," and she is in any grade from K to 2, let's say . . . (remember literacy skill does not exactly correlate with literacy ability based on chronological age or grade level for that matter, and if the student has exceptionalities, the grade can be from K to 8).

Teacher (in a quiet corner of the room): "Hi Lucy. Today I am going to play sound games with you so that I can found out exactly what kinds of sounds I need to teach you!"

Lucy: "OK." (She smiles, perhaps because the teacher set her at ease and indicated that this is a game—since the items are very game-like).

Teacher (opens her ELA & Toolbox book to page 26, "Rhyming with Simple Words!"):

Rhyming with Simple Words! -1-	
Date: Student: Teacher:	
Skill Focus: RHYME	Correct = √
Practice: *"The two words that I am going to say may or may not rhyme, so listen carefully. Do lot and pot rhyme?"* -(pause)- "Yes."	
-1- Do pat and mat rhyme? (Yes)	

"I am going to write down today's date and your name. First, to help get you ready, I am going to give you a practice question." (Teacher reads the practice question above.) "OK. Here we go! Do *pat* and *mat* rhyme?"

Gluing Words Together

Within this activity, syllables will be identified and connections made to words with similar syllable breaks. The teacher will have the students sit in a circle. A beanbag or softball will be used to toss to the next participant

How to know you were a success?

With each new word displayed, the beanbag is tossed to a new student. This continues until all have participated.

Te le phone	Mac a ro ni
Al li ga tor	Cat er pil lar
Oc to pus	Dish wash er
Ham bur ger	Com pu ter
Wa ter mel on	

Materials
◊ Word List on PowerPoint
◊ Beanbag to toss

The teacher will begin by explaining that a word will be pronounced in syllables. It is helpful to have the words in a PowerPoint presentation with each word appearing individually. Explain that as a

Lucy: "Yes."

The teacher and Lucy keep moving along. . . . Lucy gets more than 6 correct on "Rhyming with Words; Simple Sounds; and Word Count." But then on "Gluing Words Together," she gets 5 out of 10 correct.

Teacher: "Very good job Lucy! Now we are going to play more games. The games we are going to play. . . ."

The teacher turns to page 257 to the section labeled "Toolbox for Teaching Using Assessment Results" and specifically to the "Gluing Words Together" instructional game.

Teacher: "Lucy, we are going to play "Gluing Words Together," which is a game that makes you hear sounds really well!"

The teacher proceeds to play "Gluing Words Together" with Lucy. After a few sessions with Lucy playing this game, the teacher is ready to assess her again. Only now she will start "Gluing Words Together" and use the second version of that assessment, titled "Gluing Words Together-2" on page 29. (Note that the multiple versions of the same assessments are so that the students do not gain familiarity with the items, so that the results are reliable and valid.)

Gluing Words Together! -2-	
Date: Student: Teacher:	
Skill Focus: SYLLABLES	Correct = √
Practice: *"Bleed together the words that you hear (farm; house to farmhouse), segment (backbone to back; bone), or remove a word airplane without air; plane)."*	
-1- Listen to these two words: *gem; stone*. Say the entire word together (gemstone).	
-2- Listen to these two words: *hair; cut*. Say the entire word together (haircut).	

At this point the teacher is going to assess Lucy again, and this can occur periodically throughout the year, depending on the student, but at least once a month. So now the teacher will do the second assessment, starting with "Gluing Words Together" and continuing the assessment until Lucy get less than 6 correct on a form. When Lucy gets less than 6, the teacher will stop, go the instructional game with the same name as the assessment form, and play the game for teaching and reinforcement. Then the cycle of assessment begins again.

The assessment is no longer needed when students complete all items, ending with "Word Play" starting on page 154 with 6 or more correct. At this point they will need more advanced morphological instruction with the general literacy curriculum of vocabulary, word identification, and comprehension.

WHAT IS PHONOLOGICAL AWARENESS—SOUND DISCRIMINATION

Studying Sounds Leads to Achievement in Phonics and Reading

Phonological awareness is the ability to discern both individual sounds within words and the sound of whole words. PA exists in a continuum of skills from easy to difficult (see examples of PA subskills below).

Each PA subskill leads to success on the next skill, so teaching the exact PA skill a student needs will enable him or her to eventually acquire all the PA skills necessary to experience success in phonics, a key early reading skill and the foundation for decoding unfamiliar words in text.

Examples of PA subskills

Phonological "big unit" whole-word sounds:

1. *Rhyming with Simple Words!* Rhyme: Do *hat* and *cat* rhyme? (yes)
2. *Simple Sounds!* Alliteration: Do all three words start with the same sound: bat; ball; small? (yes)
3. *Word Count!* Words: How many words do you see in this sentence: The man went home. (4)
4. *Gluing Words Together!* Syllables: If you take *pig* out of *piglet*, what do you have? (let)
5. *Use Your Glue Again—Beginning Sound to Ending Sound!* Onsets and rimes: What word do these sounds put together make: b-it? (bit)

Phonemic "individual" sounds that are also inside words:

1. *Find the Sound!* Isolation: What sound do you hear at the beginning of *love*, *Lou*, and *Lacy*? (l)
2. *Find the Same Sound!* Identification: What is the same sound in the following words: cat, bite, lit? (t)
3. *Which Word Belongs!* Categorization: Which word does not belong: hat, cat, bap? (bap)
4. *Word Making Machine!* Blending: What word can you make from the following sounds: k; i; t? (kit)
5. *Sound Count!* Segmenting: How many sounds do you hear in /s/ /i/ /p/? (3)
6. *Remove the Sound!* Phoneme manipulation: Say "par." Now say "par" without the /p/ (ar)

WHAT IS MORPHOLOGICAL AWARENESS—WORD PARTS
Studying Word Parts Increases Reading Achievement

Examples of MA subskills

1. *Build the Word with Patterns!* Word analogy: Listen: "hush; hushed-push." (pushed)
2. *Word Part Remover!* Affix identification: Say "bats." Now make it a shorter word. (bat)

3. *Gluing Word Parts!* Production of multimorphemic words: Say "re." Now say "kit." Put them together. (rekit)
4. *Finish the Sentence!* Sentence analogy: That ball is so bally. That wall is so. . . . (wally)
5. *Word Play!* Defining pseudo words: The basketball player undunked the ball. (she didn't dunk it)

ELA CONNECTIONS TO STANDARDS

To discuss the alignment of these two important literacy components, a new phrase is utilized. The *Next Generation State Standards* phrase encompasses all state standards, incorporating the *Common Core State Standards* (CCSS) within the individual state standards. However, the alignment tables below reference the CCSS so that states can determine how state-specific standards align.

Alignment Introduction

The CCSS exist as a cooperative effort between the National Governors Association and the Council of Chief State School Officers. Implemented with fidelity, these standards ensure that children in every state are provided with the same set of outcomes coupled with similar academic expectations and rigorous instruction—an exciting venture! However, during the very lengthy process of writing the standards, the focus was on the transition from high school to college and career. With this focus, the emphasis on the interplay between all language systems (phonology, orthography, morphology, syntax, semantics, pragmatics, etymology, and discourse) as students learn to read, write, speak, and listen was somewhat disguised. The interplay of these language systems is crucial to early literacy development to ensure students become independent readers and writers.

The CCSS leave much to the discretion of states, districts, schools, and educators related to the foundational reading skills, as well as language skills. With a tremendous emphasis on "close reading" so that students exit grade 12 ready for college and career academic reading and writing, the requisite language skills are almost an afterthought within the CCSS. These requisite and foundation language skills are necessary for students to read and write at increasingly sophisticated levels across the grade levels. Moats (2012) argues that the CCSS "obfuscates important relationships among word recognition, spelling, fluency, and comprehension. . . . For example, from the standards document, a reader cannot learn that speech sound blending supports word recognition, that spelling supports vocabulary, that understanding morphology speeds word recognition, or that oral language capacities are the underpinning of written language" (p. 33). Thus, educators need to fully understand the mutuality of these important language systems to be able to "read between the lines" of the CCSS to ensure that students can access text in order to participate in "close reading"—the very goal of the CCSS.

Since the CCSS don't provide the emphasis on these important and foundational skills, educators must assess and provide instruction to ensure that students possess these skills. Assessing students' individual skills related to phonological and morphological awareness provides educators with the data necessary to provide instruction based on students' needs. Instruction is matched to gaps in student knowledge using teacher-directed, systematic, explicit instruction that is based on the continuum of development for each language component. Phonological awareness and morphological awareness are hugely important foundational skills to put students on a trajectory of successful reading and writing that ultimately results in accessing text to complete that "close reading" and academic-specific writing necessary for college and career attainment.

The tables below provide alignment of phonological and morphological awareness to the CCSS.

Table 1. Kindergarten Alignment[1]

Kindergarten	Phonological awareness CCSS alignment	Morphological awareness CCSS alignment
Sound discrimination — phonological awareness CCSS Reading Standards: Foundational Skills (K–5) Standard 2: Demonstrate understanding of spoken words, syllables, and sounds (phonemes). **Word parts knowledge — morphological awareness** CCSS Language Standards (K–5) Vocabulary Acquisition and Use Standard 4: Determine or clarify the meaning of unknown and multiple-meaning words and phrases based on kindergarten reading and content.	a. Recognize and produce rhyming words. b. Count, pronounce, blend, and segment syllables in a word. c. Blend and segment onset and rimes of single-syllable spoken words. d. Isolate and pronounce the initial, medial vowel, and final sounds (phonemes) in three-phoneme (consonant-vowel-consonant, or CVC) words. (This does not include CVCs ending with /l/, /r/, or /x/.) e. Add or substitute individual sounds (phonemes) in simple, one-syllable words to make new words.	Identify new meanings for familiar words and apply them accurately (e.g., knowing *duck* is a bird and learning the verb *to duck*). Use the most frequently occurring inflections and affixes (e.g., *-ed, -s, re-, un-, pre-, -ful, -less*) as a clue to the meaning of an unknown word.

---

1   Adapted from: http://www.corestandards.org/ELA-Literacy/RF/K/. Copyright © by Common Core State Standards Initiative.

Table 2. First Grade Alignment[2]

Grade 1	Phonological awareness CCSS alignment	Morphological awareness CCSS alignment
Sound discrimination—phonological awareness CCSS Reading Standards: Foundational Skills (K–5) Standard 2: Demonstrate understanding of spoken words, syllables, and sounds (phonemes).	a. Distinguish long from short vowel sounds in spoken single-syllable words.	Use sentence-level context as a clue to the meaning of a word or phrase.
	b. Orally produce single-syllable words by blending sounds (phonemes), including consonant blends.	Use frequently occurring affixes as a clue to the meaning of a word.
Word parts knowledge—morphological awareness CCSS Language Standards (K–5) Vocabulary Acquisition and Use Standard 4: Determine or clarify the meaning of unknown and multiple-meaning words and phrases based on grade 1 reading and content, choosing flexibly from an array of strategies.	c. Isolate and pronounce initial, medial vowel, and final sounds (phonemes) in spoken single-syllable words.	Identify frequently occurring root words (e.g., *look*) and their inflectional forms (e.g., *looks, looked, looking*).
	d. Segment spoken single-syllable words into their complete sequence of individual sounds (phonemes).	

Table 3. Second Grade Alignment[3]

Grade 2	Morphological awareness CCSS alignment
Sound discrimination—phonological awareness None	a. Use sentence-level context as a clue to the meaning of a word or phrase.
Word parts knowledge—morphological awareness CCSS Language Standards (K–5) Vocabulary Acquisition and Use Standard 4: Determine or clarify the meaning of unknown and multiple-meaning words and phrases based on grade 2 reading and content, choosing flexibly from an array of strategies.	b. Determine the meaning of the new word formed when a known prefix is added to a known word (e.g., *happy/unhappy, tell/retell*).
	c. Use a known root word as a clue to the meaning of an unknown word with the same root (e.g., *addition, additional*).
	d. Use knowledge of the meaning of individual words to predict the meaning of compound words (e.g., *birdhouse, lighthouse, housefly; bookshelf, notebook, bookmark*).
	e. Use glossaries and beginning dictionaries, both print and digital, to determine or clarify the meaning of words and phrases.

---

2   Adapted from: http://www.corestandards.org/ELA-Literacy/RF/1/. Copyright © by Common Core State Standards Initiative.
3   Adapted from: http://www.corestandards.org/ELA-Literacy/L/2/. Copyright © by Common Core State Standards Initiative.

Table 4. Third Grade Alignment[4]

Grade 3	Morphological awareness CCSS alignment
Sound discrimination—phonological awareness None **Word parts knowledge—morphological awareness** CCSS Language Standards (K–5) Vocabulary Acquisition and Use Standard 4: Determine or clarify the meaning of unknown and multiple-meaning words and phrases based on grade 3 reading and content, choosing flexibly from an array of strategies.	a. Use sentence-level context as a clue to the meaning of a word or phrase. b. Determine the meaning of the new word formed when a known affix is added to a known word (e.g., *agreeable/disagreeable, comfortable/uncomfortable, care/careless, heat/preheat*). c. Use a known root word as a clue to the meaning of an unknown word with the same root (e.g., *company, companion*). d. Use glossaries and beginning dictionaries, both print and digital, to determine or clarify the precise meaning of key words and phrases.

GUIDANCE FOR THE SCHOOL PRINCIPAL OR CURRICULUM LEADER IN ASSISTING TEACHER IMPLEMENTATION

For schools to have effective literacy programs that implement the CCSS with fidelity, it is important for principals to have a deep understanding of literacy instruction, have the ability to guide teachers' understanding and use of data to make instructional decisions, and implement ongoing, systematic professional development that is aligned with best practices for literacy instruction. All principals need not be reading experts; however, they must lead their teachers as proponents of effective reading instruction. Research indicates that students need instruction in five reading areas: phonemic awareness, phonics, fluency, vocabulary, and comprehension (National Reading Panel 2000). The depth of understanding principals have of the five reading areas will enhance their ability to become effective instructional leaders, and as they become more aware of the central ideas being developed and communicated by teachers in their classrooms, they will further enhance their ability to support effective reading instruction.

The Role of the Principal in Literacy Instruction

The role of the principal as the instructional leader of the school is essential to ensuring effective instruction is provided systematically to all students. The ability of the principal to observe reading instruction and provide meaningful feedback to teachers is predicated on the degree of the principal's content knowledge. Overholt and Szabocsik (2013) assert that principals need a basic knowledge of literacy content, which links instructional

---

4   Adapted from: http://www.corestandards.org/ELA-Literacy/L/3/. Copyright © by Common Core State Standards Initiative.

leadership to teaching and learning. They refer to this basic knowledge as leadership content knowledge (LCK). When principals develop a depth of LCK, they can become more sensitive observers of instruction and engage in conversations with teachers, which focus more directly on instructional practice. In a study of eighteen principals and district leaders, Overholt and Szabocsik concluded that expert principals who possess LCK:

1. make complete and meaningful comments and use the vocabulary of literacy,
2. tend to give advice and suggest ways to improve practice,
3. connect the need for resources to reading instruction, and
4. find ways to support teachers as they continue to learn in the context of their practice.

As principals' LCK deepens, they are more confident in providing meaningful feedback to teachers surrounding not only the structures and mechanics of the classroom, but more importantly on the content of the instruction and pedagogy. They can leverage a degree of expertise in literacy instruction to ensure consistency in all reading classrooms; thus ensuring the implementation of an effective reading process school-wide.

The Role of the Principal in Guiding Databased Decisions

Perceptive principals understand that some teachers are hesitant to use classroom data to guide instructional practice because they face questions and anxiety and perhaps lack the expertise. In the process of initiating databased decision making for achieving greater results in student achievement in reading, the principal must provide teachers with data in a format that they can understand and use to adjust instructional practice. Popham (1995) indicated that the purpose of classroom assessment is to improve teacher instruction. Given that, "in the hands of skilled principals and teachers, assessment data can provide important insights into student learning and guide instructional decision-making" (Fox 2013).

Just as principals and teachers work to develop a common language regarding literacy and the teaching of reading, they must also develop a common language around data and its use in guiding instructional decisions based on student needs. Fox (2013) finds there are three basic types of data around which principals and teachers should develop a shared vocabulary to understand the data and their effects on teaching and learning: outcome data, which refers to the evidence of student learning; demographic data, which refers to the variables that affect student learning; and process data, which refers to the components of instructional practice. Once this shared language is understood, conversations concerning data, instruction, and student achievement can become more productive and purposeful.

These conversations around classroom data can also lead to a deeper understanding of how to approach classroom assessments. Guskey (2003) states, "Teachers who develop useful assessments, provide corrective instruction, and give students second chances to demonstrate success can improve their instruction and help students learn." He asserts there are three important ways to use classroom assessments and data to achieve this.

1. Make Assessments Useful

Classroom assessments should reflect the concepts and skills taught in class; thus, they reflect the learning goals. Useful assessments benefit students and teachers alike by providing meaningful feedback—what has been learned, what was taught well, and what students and teachers need to work on. With this mind-set regarding assessments, "teachers and students share responsibility for learning. . . . And teachers need this kind of evidence to help target their instructional improvement efforts" (Guskey 2003, 3).

2. Follow Assessments with Corrective Instruction

When teachers view classroom assessments as opportunities for corrective action for students who haven't mastered important skills or concepts, they seek to develop alternate methods of instruction to accommodate the learning needs of their students. These teachers understand that providing time for immediate corrective action targeted on the deficit skill area(s) may position students for success in subsequent learning situations.

3. Give Second Chances to Demonstrate Success

When the goals of classroom assessments are to improve instructional strategies to meet the learning needs of all students and to allow all students to demonstrate their understanding of concepts and skills, then teachers, administrators, and students view assessments as part of the ongoing effort to help students learn. Too often educators see assessments as a one-shot experience or the sum total measure of what a student has learned. Teachers who embrace the value of the second chance can gauge the effectiveness of their corrective instruction through the success demonstrated by their students.

The principal's role is to guide teachers in the use of classroom assessment results to improve instruction and student achievement. To do this effectively, Graney and Shinn (2005) suggest teachers need ongoing support to effectively improve their instruction. Principals provide this support in two primary ways: ongoing, focused professional development and purposeful and meaningful conversations centered on classroom observations of effective instruction and student learning.

The Role of the Principal in Professional Development

The overall goal for principal leadership is to support high-quality, effective instruction that is grade appropriate and meets the learning needs of all students. For a principal to ensure quality instruction is administered consistently, Torgesen and Bryant (2004) build on the need for effective professional development by recommending adherence to the following:

1. Ensure teachers have excellent, ongoing, professional development that "goes beyond single session workshops to repeated exposures in which new teaching behaviors are learned over time in the classroom" (11).

2. Ensure teachers have adequate materials to support high-quality instruction such as interesting books at various levels of difficulty, technology and other supplemental materials, and comprehensive reading programs, which are explicit and systematic.

3. Monitor classroom instruction through regular walk-throughs focusing on "explicit, well organized, and engaging whole-group instruction . . . small-group instruction differentiated appropriately by student need . . . students involved in independent learning activities that are appropriate and engaging" (15).

Strong principal leadership is essential when ensuring an effective model for teaching reading is implemented school-wide. It is important for principals to have a deep understanding of literacy instruction, have the ability to guide teachers' understanding and use of data to make instructional decisions, and implement ongoing, systematic professional development that is aligned with best practices for literacy instruction. In doing so, a principal can work collaboratively with his or her teachers to ensure the reading instruction is effective and students are achieving understanding of CCSS in literacy instruction.

ASSESS AND THEN TEACH! DIRECTIONS FOR ASSESSMENT OF SOUND DISCRIMINATION

The assessor administers the Sound Discrimination Assessment individually to students. The assessment is made up of eleven sections with ten items per page and seven versions of each section. The eleven sections are Rhyming with Simple Words, Simple Sounds, Word Count, Gluing Words Together, Use Your Glue Again—Beginning Sound to Ending Sound, Find the Sound, Find the Same Sound, Which Word Belongs?, Word-Making Machine, Sound Count, and Remove the Sound.

Important Information about the Assessment of Sound Discrimination

Each section of the assessment has a practice test item. The assessor will begin with the practice item and make sure the student knows what is expected of him or her. The assessor will then read the test items to the student and wait for a response. The answer for each test item is listed in parentheses. If the student answers correctly, the assessor places a check mark in the box to the right of the test item. Any comments or notes the assessor has can be recorded in the section on the left of the document titled "Assessor Comments." If the student misses 3 or more of the test items on that page, the assessment should be concluded and the student should be directed to the game in the Toolbox for Teaching. If the student scores 6 or more answers correctly, then the assessor is to move on to the next page of the assessment. Continue with this process until the student does not score 6 or better on a section of the assessment.

Assessment Summary

Student responds CORRECTLY to 6 items, PROCEED to the assessment on the next page!

Student responds INCORRECTLY to 3 to 6 items, STOP assessment and go to the games in the "Toolbox for Teaching Using Assessment Results."

Sound Discrimination Assessments

Rhyming with Simple Words: In the beginning stages of phonological awareness, students often learn about rhyming words. In this section, the assessor introduces a set of simple rhyming words orally and asks the students if the words rhyme, reminding the students that they are listening to the rhyme of the words, not the beginning sound of the words. For example, students are asked to listen carefully and determine, "Do *pot* and *lot* rhyme?"

Simple Sounds: Recognizing sound is a vital part of phonological awareness, and it is important that we afford students with the opportunities to play with sound. The simple sound section allows student to explore the beginning sounds of words. The practice item requires the student to listen carefully to the beginning sound of three words. For example, the practice item states, "I am going to state three words: *mitt*; *mat*; *mud*. Do all three words start with the same sound?" Remind the students that they are specifically listening to the beginning sound of each words.

Word Count: Recognizing that there are separate words in sentences is also a stage of phonological awareness. The Word Count section calls for the student to listen to how many words are in each stated sentence. For example, the practice item asks, "How many words are in this list? *The dog ran*." Assessors should speak clearly and specifically while moving through the Word Count section.

Gluing Words Together: Blending words, segmenting words, and removing words requires the student to perform three separate skills. The practice item states, "Blend together the words that you hear (*basket*; *ball* to *basketball*), segment the words that you hear (*bedroom* to *bed*; *room*), or remove a word from the word you hear (*aircraft* without *air*; *craft*). Remind the student that blending calls for putting two words or sounds together, segmenting requires the separation of two words or sounds, and removing requires taking away a word or sound.

Use Your Glue Again—Beginning Sound to Ending Sound: Moving through activities that involve phonological awareness, it is key that students are afforded the opportunity to blend sounds together. This section requires students to blend two sounds together to make a word. For example, the practice item states, "Blend the following sounds: /b/-/ig/." Remind students that they are to listen to the two separate sounds and then push those sounds together to make a word.

Find the Sound: Listening to the sound at the begging, middle, and end of words also calls for the student to find specific sounds. The practice item asks, "What sound do you hear at the beginning of *dig*; *dot*; *dip*?"

As the assessor moves through this section, the questions then change their focus to the ending sounds of words. An example of this type of question would be, "What do you hear at the end of *cat*; *sat*; *rat*?" The final questions in this section address the middle sound of words. These questions ask the student, "What do you hear in the middle of these words?"

Find the Same Sound: This section calls for the student to find the same sound in a list of three words. The practice item states, "What sound do you hear in this list of words: *lip*; *lean*; *lad*?" Halfway through the section, the task moves to recognizing the same ending sounds of the three stated words. An example of this type of question is, "What same sound do you hear in this list of words: *put*; *hat*; *mitt*?" The end of this section focuses on the middle sound of the three given words. For example, "What same sound do you hear in this list of words: *lip*; *sit*; *hid*?"

Which Word Belongs? In this section, students must find the word that does not belong. This section addresses beginning sounds, middle sounds, and ending sounds. For example, the practice item calls for the student to answer, "Which of the following words does not belong: *jump*; *jar*; *mar*?" Remind the students that they are specifically listening for the word that does not belong because of its sound.

Word-Making Machine: This section requires the student to listen to a list of letter sounds and then put the sounds together to form a word. For example, the practice test items states, "What word can you make from putting together the following sounds: /p/ /a/ /t/?" As the student moves through the assessment, the number of letter sounds increases.

Sound Count: Students must recognize that sounds make up words. This section asks the student to listen to the stated sounds and then state how many sounds are in the word. The practice test item states, "How many sounds do you hear in the following word: /h/ /a/ /t/?" As the section continues, the number of sounds increases.

Remove the Sound: The final section of the Phonological Awareness Assessment calls for the student to remove a sound in each stated word. For example, the assessor would state, "Say *car* without the /c/ at the beginning." As the student moves through the assessment, each task becomes increasingly more difficult. For example, the assessor would state, "Say *bake* with a /c/ instead of a /b/."
-Grade Levels and Ranges and Students with Exceptionalities

Grades Pre-K–3 and for students with reading difficulty.
-Procedures: The assessor will explain to the students that he or she is going to learn about their knowledge of sounds and words by asking the students some questions. For each question type, the assessor will read

the example outlined at the top of the page. Each page contains a subset skill. The assessments should be administered to each individual student in a quit area.

-Scoring to Identify Teaching Level

When a student is unable to answer 6 out of 10 questions correctly, the assessor should stop assessment and proceed to the Toolbox section of the book to teach the necessary skill to the student.

Sound Discrimination Assessment versions 1–7

When a student is unable to answer 6 out of 10 questions correctly, the assessor should stop assessment and proceed to the Toolbox section of the book to teach the necessary skill to the student.

ASSESS AND THEN TEACH! DIRECTIONS FOR ASSESSMENT OF WORD PARTS STUDY

Overview

The Word Part portion of the assessment is administered individually to students by the evaluator. The assessment comprises five sections with ten items per page and ten versions of each section. The sections have brief directions and a practice test item. The evaluator will begin with the practice item to ensure the student knows what is expected of him or her. After clarifying the student's understanding of the practice item, the assessor will read the test items to the student, pause for a response, and then place a check mark by each item answered correctly. If the student responds incorrectly to 4 or more items on a page, the assessment of the section is over and the next one begins. This process continues until all five sections have been scored.

Assessment Summary

Student responds CORRECTLY to 6 items, PROCEED to the assessment on the next page!

Student responds INCORRECTLY to 3 to 6 items, STOP assessment and go to the games in the "Toolbox for Teaching Using Assessment Results."

The five sections include:

1. Build the Word with Patterns!
2. Word Part Remover!
3. Gluing Word Parts!
4. Finish the Sentence!
5. Word Play!

Directions for each section:

Build the Word with Patterns! In this section, there is a set of four words next to each number. The assessor should repeat the first three words clearly and distinctively, then ask the student to supply the final word to complete the set. The correct response is in boldfaced type. If the student answers correctly, place a check mark in the box to the right of the test item. Space is provided in the left-hand column for the assessor to record notes or observations during the assessment.

Word Part Remover! Read the pseudo word for each item and wait for the student to give you the shortened version of the pseudo word which has had the affixes removed. The answer is in boldfaced type. Mark the correct responses with a check mark in the box on the right. Again, the test section continues until the student has missed half or more of the test items on that page. When that number has been reached, move to the next section.

Gluing Word Parts! Slowly, say the parts of the word and the student will repeat the parts. The student then combines the parts to make a real word or pseudo word. The answers are in parentheses at the end of the item line. Mark the correct responses in the boxes to the right. If a student responds incorrectly to 5 or more items, the assessor should move to the next section.

Finish the Sentence! The assessor is provided with a series of four short sentences. The assessor reads the first set of sentences and pauses; then the assessor reads the first sentence in the second set, followed with a reading of part of the second, waiting for the student to complete the sentence. The student should give you the answer that is in boldfaced type at the end of the test item. Mark the correct responses with a check mark in the box and continue until half or more items are missed in this section. Move to the next section and begin.

Word Play! Read the sentence containing pseudo words with real affixes for the student. The student will tell what the sentence means by using the prefix meanings. The student should offer a negative response. Mark the correct responses with a check mark in the box and continue until half or more items are missed in this section.

-Grade Levels and Ranges and Students with Exceptionalities

Grades 2–6

-Procedures

The assessor will explain to the students that he or she is going to learn about their knowledge of sounds and words by asking the students some questions. For each question type, the assessor will read the example outlined at the top of the page. Each page contains a set of subskills. The assessments should be administered to each individual student in a quiet area.

-Scoring to Identify Teaching Level

When a student is unable to answer 6 out of 10 questions correctly, the assessor should stop the assessment and proceed to the Toolbox section of the book to teach the necessary skill to the student.

Word Part Knowledge Assessment versions 1–7

When a student is unable to answer 6 out of 10 questions correctly, the assessor should stop the assessment and proceed to the Toolbox section of the book to teach the necessary skill to the student.

Toolbox for Teaching Using Assessment Results

The Toolbox contains eleven Sound Discriminations games and five Word Part games to play with whole, small-group or individual students based on their level of skill as determined by the assessment. Each game has simple-to-follow directions and can easily be adapted by the teacher or parent to make playing easier or more difficult.

-Sound Discrimination

There are eleven games for Sound Discrimination (with the same nomenclature as the assessment).

-Word Part Knowledge

There are five games for Word Study (with the same nomenclature as the assessment).

SOUND AND
WORD PLAY

SOUND DISCRIMINATION ASSESSMENT USING GAMES

Assess and Then Teach! Directions for Assessment of Phonological Awareness

The assessor administers the Phonological Awareness Assessment individually to students. The assessment is made up of eleven sections with ten items per page and seven versions of each section. The eleven sections are Rhyming with Simple Words, Simple Sounds, Word Count, Gluing Words Together, Use Your Glue Again—Beginning Sound to Ending Sound, Find the Sound, Find the Same Sound, Which Word Belongs?, Word-Making Machine, Sound Count, and Remove the Sound.

Sound Discrimination Assessment

Each section has a practice test item. The assessor will begin with the practice item and make sure the student knows what is expected of him or her. The assessor will then read the test items to the student and wait for a response. The answer for each test item is listed in parentheses. If the student answers correctly, the assessor places a check mark in the box to the right of the text item. Any comments or notes the assessor has can be recorded in the section on the left of the document titled "Assessor Comments." If the student misses half or more of the test items on that page, the assessment should be concluded. If the student scores 6 or more answers correctly, then the assessor is to move on to the next page of the assessment. Continue with this process until the student does not score 6 or better on a section of the assessment.

Phonological—Big Units of Sound

Rhyming with Simple Words: In the beginning stages of phonological awareness, we often begin with teaching students about rhyming words. This section addresses simple rhyming word by stating two words and then asking the student if both of the words rhyme. For example, the practice item reminds the student to listen carefully, and then asks the student "Do *pot* and *lot* rhyme?" Remind the students that they are listening to the rhyme of the words, not the beginning sound of the words.

Simple Sounds: Recognizing sound is a vital part of phonological awareness, and it is important that we afford students with the opportunities to play with sound. The simple sound section allows the student to explore the beginning sounds of words. The practice item requires the student to listen carefully to the beginning sound of three words. For example, the practice item states, "I am going to stay three words: *mitt; mat; mud*. Do all three words start with the same sound?" Remind the student that they are specifically listening only to the beginning sound of the three words.

Word Count: Recognizing that there are separate words in sentences is also a stage of phonological awareness. The Word Count section calls for the student to listen to how many words are in each stated sentence. For example, the practice item asks, "How many words are in this list? *The dog ran.*" Be sure to speak clearly and specifically while moving through the Word Count section.

Gluing Words Together: Blending words, segmenting words, and removing words requires the student to perform three separate skills. The practice item states, "Blend together the words that you hear (*basket; ball* to *basketball*, segment (*bedroom* to *bed; room*), or remove a word (*aircraft* without *air; craft*). Remind the student that blending calls for putting two words or sounds together, segmenting requires the separation of two words or sounds, and removing requires taking away a word or sound.

Use Your Glue Again—Beginning Sound to Ending Sound: As we move through activities that involve phonological awareness, it is key that students are afforded the opportunity to blend sounds together. This section calls for the student to blend two sounds together to make a word. For example, the practice item states, "Blend the fowling sounds: /b/-/ig/." Remind students that they are to listen to the two separate sounds and then push those sounds together to make a word.

Phonemic—Individual Units of Sound

Find the Sound: Listening to the sound at the begging, middle, and end of words also calls for the student to find specific sounds. The practice item asks, "What sound do you hear at the beginning of *dig; dot; dip*?" As the assessor moves through this section, the questions then change their focus to the ending sounds of words. An example of this type of question would be, "What do you hear at the end of *cat; sat; rat*?" The final questions in this section address the middle sound of words. These questions ask the student, "What do you hear in the middle of these words?"

Find the Same Sound: This section calls for the student to find the same sound in a list of three words. The practice item states, "What sound do you hear in this list of words: *lip, lean, lad*?" Halfway through the section, the task moves to recognizing the same ending sounds of the three stated words. An example of this type of question is, "What same sound do you hear in this list of words: *put; hat; mitt*?" The end of this section focuses on the middle sound of the three given words. For example, "What same sound do you hear in this list of words: *lip; sit; hid*?"

Which Word Belongs? In this section, students must find the word that does not belong. This section addresses beginning sounds, middle sounds, and ending sounds. For example, the practice item calls for the student to answer, "Which of the following words does not belong: *jump; jar; mar*?" Remind students that they are specifically listening for the word that does not belong because of its sound.

Word-Making Machine: This section requires the student to listen to a list of letter sounds and then put the sounds together to form a word. For example, the practice test items states, "What word can you make from putting together the following sounds: /p/ /a/ /t/?" As the student moves through the assessment, the number of sounds increases.

Sound Count: Students must recognize that sounds make up words. This section asks the student to listen to the stated sounds and then state how many sounds are in the word. The practice test item states, "How many sounds do you hear in the following word: /h/ /a/ /t/?" As the section continues, the number of sounds increases.

Remove the Sound: The final section of the Phonological Awareness Assessment calls for the student to remove a sound in each stated word. For example, the assessor would state, "Say *car* without the /c/ at the beginning." As the student moves through the assessment, the task gets more difficult. For example, the assessor would state, "Say *bake* with a /c/ instead of a /b/."

Rhyming with Simple Words! -1-	
Date: Student: Teacher:	
Skill Focus: RHYME	**Correct = √**
Practice: ***"The two words that I am going to say may or may not rhyme, so listen carefully. Do lot and pot rhyme?"*** (pause) ***"Yes."***	
-1- Do pat and mat rhyme? (Yes)	
-2- Do sit and bit rhyme? (Yes)	
-3- Do car and rat rhyme? (No)	
-4- Do lap and sip rhyme? (No)	
-5- Do land and hand rhyme? (Yes)	
-6- Do tend and bend rhyme? (Yes)	
-7- Do bake and bike rhyme? (No)	
-8- Do bippert and mippert rhyme? (Yes)	
-9- Do lupper and lipper rhyme? (No)	
-10- Do pilner and dilner rhyme? (Yes)	

Simple Sounds! -1-	
Date: Student: Teacher:	
Skill Focus: ALLITERATION	Correct = √
Practice: *"I am going to say three words: mitt; mat; mud. Do all three words start with the same sound?"* (pause) *"Yes."*	
-1- (/d/) Do all three of these words start with the same sound: dog; dig; bag? (No)	
-2- (/b/) Do all three of these words start with the same sound: big; bed; bad? (Yes)	
-3- (/c/) Do all three of these words start with the same sound: cat; cup; can? (Yes)	
-4- (/n/) Do all three of these words start with the same sound: nap; nod; mop? (No)	
-5- (/sn/) Do all three of these words start with the same sound: snap; snail; snout? (Yes)	
-6- (/cl/) Do all three of these words start with the same sound: cloud; clown; bark? (No)	
-7- (/bl) Do all three of these words start with the same sound: black; blue; bland? (Yes)	
-8- (sh/) Do all three of these words start with the same sound: sheep; ship; shine? (Yes)	
-9- (/ch/) Do all three of these words start with the same sound: cheap; choose; could? (No)	
-10- (oi/) Do all three of these words start with the same sound: oil; oink; oyster? (Yes)	

Word Count! -1-	
Date: Student: Teacher:	
Skill Focus: WORDS IN SENTENCES	Correct = √
Practice: *"How many words are in this list? He hit the ball."* (pause) *"4"*	
-1- How many words are in this list? The dog ran home. (4)	
-2- How many words are in this list? Tom is tall. (3)	
-3- How many words are in this list? Kim walked to school. (4)	
-4- How many words are in this list? The cat chased the mouse. (5)	
-5- How many words are in this list? My arm is broken. (4)	
-6- How many words are in this list? Sit down to eat dinner. (5)	
-7- How many words are in this list? Mom cooked eggs, bacon, and biscuits. (6)	
-8- How many words are in this list? The bird flew off the roof. (6)	
-9- How many words are in this list? The green frog jumped in the muddy puddle. (8)	
-10- How many words are in this list? Look, I am jumping very high! (6)	

Gluing Words Together! -1-	
Date: Student: Teacher:	
Skill Focus: SYLLABLES	Correct = √
Practice: *"**Blend together the words that you hear (basket; ball to basketball), segment (bedroom to bed; room), or remove a word (aircraft without air; craft).**"*	
-1- Listen to these two words: *gem; stone*. Say the entire word together (gemstone)	
-2- Listen to these two words: *hair; cut*. Say the entire word together. (haircut)	
-3- Listen to these two words: *foot; ball*. Say the entire word together. (football)	
-4- Listen to these two words: *gold; fish*. Say the entire word together. (goldfish)	
-5- What two words do you hear in *grandparent*? (grand; parent)	
-6- What two words do you hear in *jackpot*? (jack; pot)	
-7- What two words to you hear in *ladybug*? (lady; bug)	
-8- If you take *moon* out of *moonbeam* what do you have left? (beam)	
-9- If you take *night* out of *nightstand* what do you have left? (stand)	
-10- If you take *ball* out of *meatball* what do you have left? (meat)	

Use Your Glue Again—Beginning Sound to Ending Sound! -1-	
Date: Student: Teacher:	
Skill Focus: ONSET AND RIME	Correct = √
Practice: *"**Blend the following sounds: /b/-/ig/.**"* (pause) *"**big**"*	
-1- Blend the following sounds: /s/-/at/. (sat)	
-2- Blend the following sounds: /n/-/ap/. (nap)	
-3- Blend the following sounds: /t/-/on/. (ton)	
-4- Blend the following sounds: /f/-/at/. (fat)	
-5- Blend the following sounds: /m/-/oon/. (moon)	
-6- Blend the following sounds: /h/-/and/. (hand)	
-7- Blend the following sounds: /s/-/alt/. (salt)	
-8- Blend the following sounds: /bl /-/ack/. (black)	
-9- Blend the following sounds: /fr/-/og/. (frog)	
-10- Blend the following sounds: /st/-/aller/. (staller)	

<table>
<tr><td colspan="2" align="center">**Find the Sound! -1-**</td></tr>
<tr><td colspan="2">Date: Student: Teacher:</td></tr>
<tr><td>**Skill Focus: ISOLATION**</td><td>Correct = √</td></tr>
<tr><td colspan="2">**Practice: "What sound do you hear at the beginning of dig; dot; dip?"** (pause) **"/d/"** (sound, not letter)</td></tr>
<tr><td>-1- What do you hear at the **beginning** of pat; pick; pot? (/p/)</td><td></td></tr>
<tr><td>-2- What do you hear at the **beginning** of back; bear; big? (/b/)</td><td></td></tr>
<tr><td>-3- What do you hear at the **beginning** of nip; nod; neck? (/n/)</td><td></td></tr>
<tr><td>-4- What do you hear at the **beginning** of lid; lock; loan? (/l/)</td><td></td></tr>
<tr><td>-5- What do you hear at the **end** of cat; sat; rat? (/t/)</td><td></td></tr>
<tr><td>-6- What do you hear at the **end** of face; place; case? (/s/)</td><td></td></tr>
<tr><td>-7- What do you hear at the **end** of load; mode; toad? (/d/)</td><td></td></tr>
<tr><td>-8- What do you hear in the **middle** of sip; tip; nip? (/i/)</td><td></td></tr>
<tr><td>-9- What do you hear in the **middle** of mutt; put; cut? (/u/)</td><td></td></tr>
<tr><td>-10- What do you hear in the **middle** of coat; moat; boat? (/oa/) (Pronounce complex vowel sound of /oa/ as long vowel o.)</td><td></td></tr>
</table>

<table>
<tr><td colspan="2" align="center">**Find the Same Sound! -1-**</td></tr>
<tr><td colspan="2">Date: Student: Teacher:</td></tr>
<tr><td>**Skill Focus: IDENTITY**</td><td>Correct = √</td></tr>
<tr><td colspan="2">**Practice: "What same sound do you hear in this list of words: lip; lean; lad?"** (pause) **"/l/"** (sound, not letter)</td></tr>
<tr><td>-1- What same sound do you hear in this list of words: nap; not; Nick? (/n/)</td><td></td></tr>
<tr><td>-2- What same sound do you hear in this list of words: lad; lip; luck? (/l/)</td><td></td></tr>
<tr><td>-3- What same sound do you hear in this list of words: dark; dip; dog? (/d/)</td><td></td></tr>
<tr><td>-4- What same sound do you hear in this list of words: umbrella; under; us? (/u/)</td><td></td></tr>
<tr><td>-5- What same sound do you hear in this list of words: put; hat; mitt? (/t/)</td><td></td></tr>
<tr><td>-6- What same sound do you hear in this list of words: sad; could; dud? (/d/)</td><td></td></tr>
<tr><td>-7- What same sound do you hear in this list of words: Tom; ham; dim? (/m/)</td><td></td></tr>
<tr><td>-8- What same sound do you hear in this list of words: lip; sit; hid? (/i/) (short i)</td><td></td></tr>
<tr><td>-9- What same sound do you hear in this list of words: pot; knob; fox? (/o/) (short o)</td><td></td></tr>
<tr><td>-10- What same sound do you hear in this list of words: pad; sat; rack? (/a/) (short a)</td><td></td></tr>
</table>

Which Word Belongs? -1-

	Correct = √
Date: Student: Teacher:	
Skill Focus: CATEGORIZATION	
Practice: *"Which of the following words does not belong: jump; jar; mar?* (pause) *"mar"*	
-1- Which of the following words does not belong: sick; David; sad? (David)	
-2- Which of the following words does not belong: lad; lick; cake? (cake)	
-3- Which of the following words does not belong: sud; kick; kite? (sud)	
-4- Which of the following words does not belong: tack; back; nap? (nap)	
-5- Which of the following words does not belong: pull; shoe; fill? (shoe)	
-6- Which of the following words does not belong: tot; men; pin? (tot)	
-7- Which of the following words does not belong: pill; mull; note? (note)	
-8- Which of the following words does not belong: ran; mutt; bub? (ran)	
-9- Which of the following words does not belong: pat; lim; tam? (lim)	
-10- Which of the following words does not belong: sip; hit; tock? (tock)	

Word-Making Machine! -1-

	Correct = √
Date: Student: Teacher:	
Skill Focus: BLENDING	
Practice: *"What word can you make from putting together the following sounds: /p/ /a/ /t/ ?* (pause) *"pat"*	
-1- What word can you make from putting together the following sounds: /p/ /u/ /ll/? (pull)	
-2- What word can you make from putting together the following sounds: /s/ /i/ /n/? (sin)	
-3- What word can you make from putting together the following sounds: /t/ /a/ /p/? (tap)	
-4- What word can you make from putting together the following sounds: /s/ /a/ /n/ /d/? (sand)	
-5- What word can you make from putting together the following sounds: /l/ /o/ /t/ /s/? (lots)	
-6- What word can you make from putting together the following sounds: /s/ /n/ /a/ /p/? (snap)	
-7- What word can you make from putting together the following sounds: /p/ /a/ /s/ /t/? (past)	
-8- What word can you make from putting together the following sounds: /m/ /a/ /k/ /r/? (maker)	
-9- What word can you make from putting together the following sounds: /t/ /i/ /n/ /t/ /r/? (tinter)	
-10- What word can you make from putting together the following sounds: /s/ /l/ /ee/ /p/ /r/? (sleeper)	

Sound Count! -1-	
Date: Student: Teacher:	
Skill Focus: SEGMENTING	Correct = √
Practice: *"How many sounds do you hear in the following word? /h/ /a/ /t/?* (pause) *"3"*	
-1- How many sounds do you hear in the following word: /j/ /a/ /m/? (jam) (3)	
-2- How many sounds do you hear in the following word: /o/ /n/? (on) (2)	
-3- How many sounds do you hear in the following word: /n/ /i/ /p/? (nip) (3)	
-4- How many sounds do you hear in the following word: /s/ /c/ /a/ /b/? (scab) (4)	
-5- How many sounds do you hear in the following word: /c/ /l/ /a/ /p/? (clap) (4)	
-6- How many sounds do you hear in the following word: /b/ /u/ /m/ /p/? (bump) (4)	
-7- How many sounds do you hear in the following word: /d/ /a/ /r/ /k/? (dark) (4)	
-8- How many sounds do you hear in the following word: /r/ /u/ /p/ /r/ /t/? (ruppert) (5)	
-9- How many sounds do you hear in the following word: /b/ /a/ /k/ /r/? (baker) (4)	
-10- How many sounds do you hear in the following word: /s/ /a/ /p/ /r/ /z/? (sapers) (5)	

Remove the Sound! -1-	
Date: Student: Teacher:	
Skill Focus: MANIPULATION	Correct = √
Practice: "Say car **without the /c/ at the beginning. You would say"** (pause) **"/r/."**	
-1- Say *hat* without the /h/ (at).	
-2- Say *mit* without the /m/ (it).	
-3- Say *at* without the /a/ (t).	
-4- Say *skit* without the /t/ (ski).	
-5- Say *cast* without the /s/ (cat).	
-6- Say *hunt* without the /n/ (hut).	
-7- Say *jist* without the /s/ (jit).	
-8- Say *at* with an /m/ at the beginning (mat).	
-9- Say *it* with a /p/ at the beginning (pit).	
-10- Say *bake* with a /c/ instead of a /b/ (cake).	

Rhyming with Simple Words! -2-	
Date: Student: Teacher:	
Skill Focus: RHYME	Correct = √
Practice: ***"The two words that I am going to say may or may not rhyme, so listen carefully. Do kid and lid rhyme?"*** (pause) ***"Yes."***	
-1- Do top and hop rhyme? (Yes)	
-2- Do bat and cat rhyme? (Yes)	
-3- Do sat and rip rhyme? (No)	
-4- Do lick and did rhyme? (No)	
-5- Do lock and rock rhyme? (Yes)	
-6- Do lend and send rhyme? (Yes)	
-7- Do rake and ripe rhyme? (No)	
-8- Do supper and lupper rhyme? (Yes)	
-9- Do tipper and muppet rhyme? (No)	
-10- Do dance and prance rhyme? (Yes)	

Simple Sounds! -2-	
Date: Student: Teacher:	
Skill Focus: ALLITERATION	Correct = √
Practice: ***"I am going to say three words: mad; mitt; mop. Do all three words start with the same sound?"*** (pause) ***"Yes."***	
-1- (/f/) Do all three of these words start with the same sound: fat; fog; pat? (No)	
-2- (/b/) Do all three of these words start with the same sound: beg; back; bark? (Yes)	
-3- (/t/) Do all three of these words start with the same sound: tap; tick; tar? (Yes)	
-4- (/d/) Do all three of these words start with the same sound: door; bed; big? (No)	
-5- (/pl/) Do all three of these words start with the same sound: place; plot; plain? (Yes)	
-6- (/tr/) Do all three of these words start with the same sound: train; pick; tree? (No)	
-7- (sn) Do all three of these words start with the same sound: snap; snout; sneeze? (Yes)	
-8- (/gl/) Do all three of these words start with the same sound: glaze; glad; gleam? (Yes)	
-9- (/sm/) Do all three of these words start with the same sound: smack; smart; cloud? (No)	
-10- (/sc/) Do all three of these words start with the same sound: scrap; screen; scram? (Yes)	

Word Count! -2-	
Date: Student: Teacher:	
Skill Focus: WORDS IN SENTENCES	Correct = √
Practice: *"How many words are in this list? The dog ran."* (pause) *"3"*	
-1- How many words are in this list? The frog jumped high. (4)	
-2- How many words are in this list? She went home. (3)	
-3- How many words are in this list? Kate walked to the park. (5)	
-4- How many words are in this list? He went to the doctor. (5)	
-5- How many words are in this list? Sam kicked the ball. (4)	
-6- How many words are in this list? Sit down to watch television. (5)	
-7- How many words are in this list? Dad drove the car to work. (6)	
-8- How many words are in this list? The big spider is hairy. (5)	
-9- How many words are in this list? The boys raced down the street. (6)	
-10- How many words are in this list? Watch me jump off the diving board. (7)	

Gluing Words Together! -2-	
Date: Student: Teacher:	
Skill Focus: SYLLABLES	Correct = √
Practice: *"Blend together the words that you hear (farm; house to farmhouse), segment (backbone to back; bone), or remove a word (airplane without air; plane)."*	
-1- Listen to these two words: *gem; stone*. Say the entire word together. (gemstone)	
-2- Listen to these two words: *hair; cut*. Say the entire word together. (haircut)	
-3- Listen to these two words: *foot; ball*. Say the entire word together. (football)	
-4- Listen to these two words: *gold; fish*. Say the entire word together. (goldfish)	
-5- What two words do you hear in *grandparent*? (grand; parent)	
-6- What two words do you hear in *jackpot*? (jack; pot)	
-7- What two words to you hear in *ladybug*? (lady; bug)	
-8- If you take *moon* out of *moonbeam* what do you have left? (beam)	
-9- If you take *night* out of *nightstand* what do you have left? (stand)	
-10- If you take *ball* out of *meatball* what do you have left? (meat)	

Use Your Glue Again—Beginning Sound to Ending Sound! -2-	
Date: Student: Teacher:	
Skill Focus: ONSET AND RIME	**Correct = √**
Practice: *"Blend the following sounds: /p/-/ig/."* (pause) *"pig"*	
-1- Blend the following sounds: /s/-/at/. (sat)	
-2- Blend the following sounds: /n/-/ap/. (nap)	
-3- Blend the following sounds: /t/-/on/. (ton)	
-4- Blend the following sounds: /f/-/at/. (fat)	
-5- Blend the following sounds: /m/-/oon/. (moon)	
-6- Blend the following sounds: /h/-/and/. (hand)	
-7- Blend the following sounds: /s/-/alt/. (salt)	
-8- Blend the following sounds: /bl/-/ack/. (black)	
-9- Blend the following sounds: /fr/-/og/. (frog)	
-10- Blend the following sounds: /st/-/aller/. (staller)	

Find the Sound! -2-	
Date: Student: Teacher:	
Skill Focus: ISOLATION	**Correct = √**
Practice: *"What sound do you hear at the beginning of dig; dot; dip?"* (pause) *"/d/"* (sound, not letter)	
-1- What do you hear at the **beginning** of pad; pock; pop? (/p/)	
-2- What do you hear at the **beginning** of bat; beg; bot? (/b/)	
-3- What do you hear at the **beginning** of car; cup; cost? (/c/)	
-4- What do you hear at the **beginning** of lip; lot; luck? (/l/)	
-5- What do you hear at the **end** of tiff; riff; miff? (/f/)	
-6- What do you hear at the **end** of note; cast; lift? (/t/)	
-7- What do you hear at the **end** of fold; road; mode? (/d/)	
-8- What do you hear in the **middle** of slip; fit; bib? (/i/)	
-9- What do you hear in the **middle** of puff; gut; mud? (/u/)	
-10- What do you hear in the **middle** of mad; sat; rack? (/a/)	

Find the Same Sound! -2-

Date: Student: Teacher:	
Skill Focus: IDENTITY	Correct = √
Practice: *"What same sound do you hear in this list of words: lip; lean; lad?* (pause) *"/l/"* (sound, not letter)	
-1- What same sound do you hear in this list of words: back; bed; box? (/b/)	
-2- What same sound do you hear in this list of words: pad; pot; pick? (/p/)	
-3- What same sound do you hear in this list of words: dig; dagger; dot? (/d/)	
-4- What same sound do you hear in this list of words: fox; fan; fit? (/f/)	
-5- What same sound do you hear in this list of words: tram; mim; hum? (/m/)	
-6- What same sound do you hear in this list of words: hiss; moss; class? (/s/)	
-7- What same sound do you hear in this list of words: hot; what; mutt? (/t/)	
-8- What same sound do you hear in this list of words: bed; set; Rex? (/e/) (short e)	
-9- What same sound do you hear in this list of words: hut; nut; lut? (/u/) (short u)	
-10- What same sound do you hear in this list of words: rad; sat; tack? (/a/) (short a)	

Which Word Belongs? -2-

Date: Student: Teacher:	
Skill Focus: CATEGORIZATION	Correct = √
Practice: *"Which of the following words does not belong: jump; jar; mar?* (pause) *"mar"*	
-1- Which of the following words does not belong: song; Jack; sit? (Jack)	
-2- Which of the following words does not belong: keep; kite; gate? (gate)	
-3- Which of the following words does not belong: car; sip; come? (sip)	
-4- Which of the following words does not belong: lack; pack; map? (map)	
-5- Which of the following words does not belong: bike; shop; hike? (shop)	
-6- Which of the following words does not belong: neat; heat; pack? (pack)	
7- Which of the following words does not belong: nice; fill; tall? (nice)	
-8- Which of the following words does not belong: rake; tube; rude? (rake)	
-9- Which of the following words does not belong: rock; sock; limb? (limb)	
-10- Which of the following words does not belong: ring; flake; tick? (flake)	

Word-Making Machine! -2-	
Date: Student: Teacher:	
Skill Focus: BLENDING	**Correct = √**
Practice: ***"What word can you make from putting together the following sounds: /p/ /a/ /t/?"*** (pause) ***"pat"***	
-1- What word can you make from putting together the following sounds: /f/ /u/ /ll/? (full)	
-2- What word can you make from putting together the following sounds: /t/ /i/ /n/? (tin)	
-3- What word can you make from putting together the following sounds: /l/ /a/ /p/? (lap)	
-4- What word can you make from putting together the following sounds: /h/ /a/ /n/ /d/? (hand)	
-5- What word can you make from putting together the following sounds: /p/ /o/ /t/ /s/? (pots)	
-6- What word can you make from putting together the following sounds: /c/ /l/ /a/ /p/? (clap)	
-7- What word can you make from putting together the following sounds: /l/ /a/ /s/ /t/? (last)	
-8- What word can you make from putting together the following sounds: /t/ /a/ /k/ /r/ ? (taker)	
-9- What word can you make from putting together the following sounds: /m/ /i/ /n/ /t/ /r/? (minter)	
-10- What word can you make from putting together the following sounds: /k/ /ee/ /p/ /r/? (keeper)	

Sound Count! -2-	
Date: Student: Teacher:	
Skill Focus: SEGMENTING	**Correct = √**
Practice: ***"How many sounds do you hear in the following word? /h/ /a/ /t/?"*** (pause) ***"3"***	
-1- How many sounds do you hear in the following word: /r/ /a/ /m/? (ram) (3)	
-2- How many sounds do you hear in the following word: /a/ /t/? (at) (2)	
-3- How many sounds do you hear in the following word: /l/ /i/ /p/? (lip) (3)	
-4- How many sounds do you hear in the following word: /c/ /r/ /a/ /b/? (crab) (4)	
-5- How many sounds do you hear in the following word: /s/ /l/ /a/ /p/? (slap) (4)	
-6- How many sounds do you hear in the following word: /l/ /u/ /m/ /p/? (lump) (4)	
-7- How many sounds do you hear in the following word: /p/ /a/ /r/ /k/? (park) (4)	
-8- How many sounds do you hear in the following word: /b/ /u/ /p/ /r/ /t/? (buppert) (5)	
-9- How many sounds do you hear in the following word: /m/ /a/ /k/ /r/? (maker) (4)	
-10- How many sounds do you hear in the following word: /v/ /a/ /p/ /r/ /z/? (vapers) (5)	

Remove the Sound! -2-	
Date: Student: Teacher:	
Skill Focus: MANIPULATION	Correct = √
Practice: *"Say car without the /c/ at the beginning. You would say"* (pause) *"/r/."*	
-1- Say *mat* without the /m/. (at)	
-2- Say *hit* without the /h/. (it)	
-3- Say *not* without the /n/. (ot)	
-4- Say *flirt* without the /f/. (lirt)	
-5- Say *last* without the /l/. (ast)	
-6- Say tramp without the /t/. (ramp)	
-7- Say *list* without the /s/. (lit)	
-8- Say *at* with a /p/ at the beginning. (pat)	
-9- Say *it* with an /f/ at the beginning. (fit)	
-10- Say *cake* with a /b/ instead of a /c/. (bake)	

Rhyming with Simple Words! -3-	
Date: Student: Teacher:	
Skill Focus: RHYME	Correct = √
Practice: *"The two words that I am going to say may or may not rhyme, so listen carefully. Do lot and pot rhyme?"* (pause) *"Yes."*	
-1- Do mop and bop rhyme? (Yes)	
-2- Do bat and hat rhyme? (Yes)	
-3- Do pod and lip rhyme? (No)	
-4- Do tick and sick rhyme? (Yes)	
-5- Do block and clock rhyme? (Yes)	
-6- Do sand and hike rhyme? (No)	
-7- Do land and frame rhyme? (No)	
-8- Do filter and silter rhyme? (Yes)	
-9- Do bipper and puppet rhyme? (No)	
-10- Do sipper and zipper rhyme? (Yes)	

Simple Sounds! -3-	
Date: Student: Teacher:	
Skill Focus: ALLITERATION	**Correct = √**
Practice: ***"I am going to say three words: mitt; mat; mud. Do all three words start with the same sound?"*** (pause) ***"Yes."***	
-1- (/s/) Do all three of these words start with the same sound: sip; sand; clap? (No)	
-2- (/b/) Do all three of these words start with the same sound: band; big; bird? (Yes)	
-3- (/k/) Do all three of these words start with the same sound: king; kiss; kite? (Yes)	
-4- (/m/) Do all three of these words start with the same sound: mock; mat; note? (No)	
-5- (/pl/) Do all three of these words start with the same sound: plop; please; plaid? (Yes)	
-6- (/cl/) Do all three of these words start with the same sound: clap; sip; clue? (No)	
-7- (/dr/) Do all three of these words start with the same sound: drab; drift; drawer? (Yes)	
-8- (/ch/) Do all three of these words start with the same sound: chart; cheap; charm? (Yes)	
-9- (/fl/) Do all three of these words start with the same sound: flair; eat; flat? (No)	
-10- (/gl/) Do all three of these words start with the same sound: glaze; glee; glide? (Yes)	

Word Count! -3-	
Date: Student: Teacher:	
Skill Focus: WORDS IN SENTENCES	**Correct = √**
Practice: ***"How many words are in this list? The cat pounced."*** (pause) ***"3"***	
-1- How many words are in this list? The tiny dog barked. (4)	
-2- How many words are in this list? He ran fast. (3)	
-3- How many words are in this list? They raced down the road. (5)	
-4- How many words are in this list? She listened to the teacher. (5)	
-5- How many words are in this list? Rod walked quickly. (3)	
-6- How many words are in this list? Please stay off the stage. (5)	
-7- How many words are in this list? The ocean had large waves. (5)	
-8- How many words are in this list? The kids raced to the park. (6)	
-9- How many words are in this list? John kicked the ball hard. (5)	
-10- How many words are in this list? Watch out for that big truck! (6)	

Gluing Words Together! -3-

	Correct = √
Date: Student: Teacher:	
Skill Focus: SYLLABLES	Correct = √
Practice: *"Blend together the words that you hear (basket; ball to basketball), segment (bedroom to bed; room), or remove a word (aircraft without air; craft)."*	
-1- Listen to these two words: *key; board*. Say the entire word together. (keyboard)	
-2- Listen to these two words: *butter; fly*. Say the entire word together. (butterfly)	
-3- Listen to these two words: *earth; quake*. Say the entire word together. (earthquake)	
-4- Listen to these two words: *back; bone*. Say the entire word together. (backbone)	
-5- What two words do you hear in *moonlight*? (moon; light)	
-6- What two words do you hear in *fireworks*? (fire; works)	
-7- What two words to you hear in *backward*? (back; ward)	
-8- If you take *sea* out of *seashore* what do you have left? (shore)	
-9- If you take *fall* out of *waterfall* what do you have left? (water)	
-10- If you take *super* out of *supermarket* what do you have left? (market)	

Use Your Glue Again—Beginning Sound to Ending Sound! -3-

	Correct = √
Date: Student: Teacher:	
Skill Focus: ONSET AND RIME	Correct = √
Practice: *"Blend the following sounds: /b/-/ig/."* (pause) *"big"*	
-1- Blend the following sounds: /l/-/ap/. (lap)	
-2- Blend the following sounds: /t/-/ip/. (tip)	
-3- Blend the following sounds: /f/-/un/. (fun)	
-4- Blend the following sounds: /l/-/ast/. (last)	
-5- Blend the following sounds: /sp/-/oon/. (spoon)	
-6- Blend the following sounds: /f/-/arm/. (farm)	
-7- Blend the following sounds: /sl/-/ap/. (slap)	
-8- Blend the following sounds: /cr /-/own/. (crown)	
-9- Blend the following sounds: /fr/-/ee/. (free)	
-10- Blend the following sounds: /st/-/inger/. (stinger)	

Find the Sound! -3-	
Date: Student: Teacher:	
Skill Focus: ISOLATION	**Correct = √**
Practice: ***"What sound do you hear at the beginning of dig; dot; dip?"*** (pause) ***"/d/"*** (sound, not letter)	
-1- What do you hear at the **beginning** of bed; back; bit? (/b/)	
-2- What do you hear at the **beginning** of post; peg; pat? (/p/)	
-3- What do you hear at the **beginning** of kid; kiss; kite? (/k/)	
-4- What do you hear at the **beginning** of boat; big; bear? (/b/)	
-5- What do you hear at the **end** of race; space; lace? (/s/)	
-6- What do you hear at the **end** of cuff; enough; loaf? (/f/)	
-7- What do you hear at the **end** of mold; toad; rode? (/d/)	
-8- What do you hear in the **middle** of shut; bulb; cut? (/u/)	
-9- What do you hear in the **middle** of frog; bot; pod? (/o/)	
-10- What do you hear in the **middle** of pad; fat; slack? (/a/)	

Find the Same Sound! -3-	
Date: Student: Teacher:	
Skill Focus: IDENTITY	**Correct = √**
Practice: ***"What same sound do you hear in this list of words: lip; lean; lad?"*** (pause) ***"/l/"*** (sound, not letter)	
-1- What same sound do you hear in this list of words: dock; deer; doll? (/d/)	
-2- What same sound do you hear in this list of words: lip; lug; last? (/l/)	
-3- What same sound do you hear in this list of words: sip; sat; soar? (/s/)	
-4- What same sound do you hear in this list of words: fat; fox; flip? (/f/)	
-5- What same sound do you hear in this list of words: worm; mum; come? (/m/)	
-6- What same sound do you hear in this list of words: miss; jabs; lass? (/s/)	
-7- What same sound do you hear in this list of words: not; hat; putt? (/t/)	
-8- What same sound do you hear in this list of words: red; pet; flex? (/e/) (short e)	
-9- What same sound do you hear in this list of words: lid; fist; pit? (/i/) (short i)	
-10- What same sound do you hear in this list of words: ham; pat; rack? (/a/) (short a)	

Which Word Belongs? -3-

Date:	Student:	Teacher:	
Skill Focus: CATEGORIZATION			Correct = √
Practice: "Which of the following words does not belong: jump; jar; mar?" (pause) **"mar"**			
-1- Which of the following words does not belong: sip; can; sock? (can)			
-2- Which of the following words does not belong: geese; gate; jar? (jar)			
-3- Which of the following words does not belong: cap; shape; cane? (shape)			
-4- Which of the following words does not belong: maze; mad; lack? (lack)			
-5- Which of the following words does not belong: trike; shed; like? (shed)			
-6- Which of the following words does not belong: pack; back; touch? (touch)			
-7- Which of the following words does not belong: mice; fall; mall? (mice)			
-8- Which of the following words does not belong: take; rake; snap? (snap)			
-9- Which of the following words does not belong: fan; sat; climb? (climb)			
-10- Which of the following words does not belong: fling; bake; ring? (bake)			

Word-Making Machine! -3-

Date:	Student:	Teacher:	
Skill Focus: BLENDING			Correct = √
Practice: "What word can you make from putting together the following sounds: /p/ /a/ /t/?" (pause) **"pat"**			
-1- What word can you make from putting together the following sounds: /m/ /e/ /m/? (mem)			
-2- What word can you make from putting together the following sounds: /p/ /i/ /n/? (pin)			
-3- What word can you make from putting together the following sounds: /s/ /a/ /p/? (sap)			
-4- What word can you make from putting together the following sounds: /l/ /a/ /n/ /d/? (land)			
-5- What word can you make from putting together the following sounds: /d/ /o/ /t/ /s/? (dots)			
-6- What word can you make from putting together the following sounds: /s/ /l/ /a/ /p/? (slap)			
-7- What word can you make from putting together the following sounds: /f/ /a/ /s/ /t/? (fast)			
-8- What word can you make from putting together the following sounds: /b/ /a/ /k/ /r/ ? (baker)			
-9- What word can you make from putting together the following sounds: /f/ /i/ /n/ /t/ /r/? (finter)			
-10- What word can you make from putting together the following sounds: /b/ /ee/ /p/ /r/? (beeper)			

Sound Count! -3-	
Date: Student: Teacher:	
Skill Focus: SEGMENTING	**Correct = √**
Practice: *"How many sounds do you hear in the following word? /h/ /a/ /t/?"* (pause) *"3"*	
-1- How many sounds do you hear in the following word: /t /a/ /m/? (tam) (3)	
-2- How many sounds do you hear in the following word: /u/ /p/? (up) (2)	
-3- How many sounds do you hear in the following word: /h/ /i/ /p/? (hip) (3)	
-4- How many sounds do you hear in the following word: /d/ /r/ /a/ /b/? (drab) (4)	
-5- How many sounds do you hear in the following word: /b/ /l/ /i/ /p/? (blip) (4)	
-6- How many sounds do you hear in the following word: /h/ /u/ /m/ /p/? (hump) (4)	
-7- How many sounds do you hear in the following word: /l/ /a/ /r/ /k/? (lark) (4)	
-8- How many sounds do you hear in the following word: /d/ /u/ /p/ /r/ /t/? (duppert) (5)	
-9- How many sounds do you hear in the following word: /l/ /a/ /k/ /r/? (laker) (4)	
-10- How many sounds do you hear in the following word: /t/ /a/ /p/ /r/ /z/? (tapers) (5)	

Remove the Sound! -3-	
Date: Student: Teacher:	
Skill Focus: MANIPULATION	**Correct = √**
Practice: *"Say car without the /c/ at the beginning. You would say"* (pause) *"/r/."*	
-1- Say *pat* without the /p/. (at)	
-2- Say *lit* without the /l/. (it)	
-3- Say *tot* without the /t/. (ot)	
-4- Say *blurt* without the /b/. (lurt)	
-5- Say *past* without the /p/. (ast)	
-6- Say ramp without the /r/. (amp)	
-7- Say *fist* without the /f/. (ist)	
-8- Say *ast* with an /l/ at the beginning. (last)	
-9- Say *at* with an /s/ at the beginning. (sat)	
-10- Say *fort* with an /s/ instead of an /f/. (sort)	

Rhyming with Simple Words! -4-	
Date: Student: Teacher:	
Skill Focus: RHYME	Correct = √
Practice: _"The two words that I am going to say may or may not rhyme, so listen carefully. Do lot and pot rhyme?"_ (pause) _"Yes."_	
-1- Do bop and pop rhyme? (Yes)	
-2- Do hit and lit rhyme? (Yes)	
-3- Do lad and nip rhyme? (No)	
-4- Do tock and dock rhyme? (Yes)	
-5- Do lock and sip rhyme? (No)	
-6- Do bike and trike rhyme? (Yes)	
-7- Do hand and Mike rhyme? (No)	
-8- Do found and mound rhyme? (Yes)	
-9- Do topper and muppet rhyme? (No)	
-10- Do lippert and bippert rhyme? (Yes)	

Simple Sounds! -4-	
Date: Student: Teacher:	
Skill Focus: ALLITERATION	Correct = √
Practice: "I am going to say three words: mitt; mat; mud. Do all three words start with the same sound?" (pause) _"Yes."_	
-1- (/d/) Do all three of these words start with the same sound: ding; dock; bat? (No)	
-2- (/f/) Do all three of these words start with the same sound: fest; food; first? (Yes)	
-3- (/k/) Do all three of these words start with the same sound: cane; kiss; kite? (Yes)	
-4- (/m/) Do all three of these words start with the same sound: made; not; my? (No)	
-5- (/bl/) Do all three of these words start with the same sound: blab; bleed; blade? (Yes)	
-6- (/sl/) Do all three of these words start with the same sound: slug; slip; care? (No)	
-7- (/dr/) Do all three of these words start with the same sound: drab; drift; drawer? (Yes)	
-8- (/ch/) Do all three of these words start with the same sound: chain; charge; chap? (Yes)	
-9- (/cr/) Do all three of these words start with the same sound: crab; sleep; crash? (No)	
-10- (/sm/) Do all three of these words start with the same sound: smart; smog; smell? (Yes)	

Word Count! -4-	
Date: Student: Teacher:	
Skill Focus: WORDS IN SENTENCES	Correct = √
Practice: *"How many words are in this list? The bird flew."* (pause) *"3"*	
-1- How many words are in this list? The little cat meowed. (4)	
-2- How many words are in this list? He sat down. (3)	
-3- How many words are in this list? Todd threw the ball. (4)	
-4- How many words are in this list? Sally swam in the ocean. (5)	
-5- How many words are in this list? Please stop running. (3)	
-6- How many words are in this list? They jumped on the bed. (5)	
-7- How many words are in this list? Walter went to the grocery store. (6)	
-8- How many words are in this list? The kids raced each other. (5)	
-9- How many words are in this list? My spelling test is tomorrow. (5)	
-10- How many words are in this list? Do not step in the mud puddle. (7)	

Gluing Words Together! -4-	
Date: Student: Teacher:	
Skill Focus: SYLLABLES	Correct = √
Practice: "*Blend together the words that you hear (basket; ball to basketball), segment (bedroom to bed; room), or remove a word (aircraft without air; craft).*"	
-1- Listen to these two words: *gear; shift*. Say the entire word together. (gearshift)	
-2- Listen to these two words: *flower; pot*. Say the entire word together. (flowerpot)	
-3- Listen to these two words: *grave; yard*. Say the entire word together (graveyard)	
-4- Listen to these two words: *fish; bowl*. Say the entire word together. (fishbowl)	
-5- What two words do you hear in *eyelash*? (eye; lash)	
-6- What two words do you hear in *flagpole*? (flag; pole)	
-7- What two words to you hear in *haystack*? (hay; stack)	
-8- If you take *hot* out of *hotdog* what do you have left? (dog)	
-9- If you take *suit* out of *jumpsuit* what do you have left? (jump)	
-10- If you take *neck* out of *necktie* what do you have left? (tie)	

Use Your Glue Again—Beginning Sound to Ending Sound! -4-	
Date: Student: Teacher:	
Skill Focus: ONSET AND RIME	Correct = √
Practice: *"Blend the following sounds: /b/-/ig/."* (pause) *"big"*	
-1- Blend the following sounds: /l/-/ip/. (lip)	
-2- Blend the following sounds: /r/-/ock/. (rock)	
-3- Blend the following sounds: /t/-/urn/. (turn)	
-4- Blend the following sounds: /f/-/ast/. (fast)	
-5- Blend the following sounds: /m/-/oon/. (moon)	
-6- Blend the following sounds: /a/-/larm/. (alarm)	
-7- Blend the following sounds: /sl/-/ed/. (sled)	
-8- Blend the following sounds: /fr /-/own/. (frown)	
-9- Blend the following sounds: /bl/-/eed/. (bleed)	
-10- Blend the following sounds: /str/-/ange/. (strange)	

Find the Sound! -4-	
Date: Student: Teacher:	
Skill Focus: ISOLATION	Correct = √
Practice: *"What sound do you hear at the beginning of dig; dot; dip?"* (pause) *"/d/"* (sound, not letter)	
-1- What do you hear at the **beginning** of dip; dock; dane? (/d/)	
-2- What do you hear at the **beginning** of lost; led; lip? (/l/)	
-3- What do you hear at the **beginning** of candy; cut; code? (/c/)	
-4- What do you hear at the **beginning** of sat; site; suds? (/s/)	
-5- What do you hear at the **end** of luck; block; chalk? (/c/)	
-6- What do you hear at the **end** of tough; fluff; tiff? (/f/)	
-7- What do you hear at the **end** of cold; red; send? (/d/)	
-8- What do you hear in the **middle** of cone; bone; tone? (/o/) (long o)	
-9- What do you hear in the **middle** of box; pot; job? (/o/)	
-10- What do you hear in the **middle** of pad; mat; lack? (/a/)	

Find the Same Sound! -4-	
Date: Student: Teacher:	
Skill Focus: IDENTITY	**Correct = √**
Practice: *"What same sound do you hear in this list of words: lip; lean; lad?"* (pause) *"/l/"* (sound, not letter)	
-1- What same sound do you hear in this list of words: apple; ant; alligator? (/a/) (short a)	
-2- What same sound do you hear in this list of words: under; ultra; up? (/u/)	
-3- What same sound do you hear in this list of words: mop; make; might? (/m/)	
-4- What same sound do you hear in this list of words: tap; tough; tilt? (/t/)	
-5- What same sound do you hear in this list of words: moist; taint; bait? (/t/)	
-6- What same sound do you hear in this list of words: kiss; hose; pass? (/s/)	
-7- What same sound do you hear in this list of words: candy; pity; putty? (/e/) (long e)	
-8- What same sound do you hear in this list of words: happen; tad; ham? (/a/) (short a)	
-9- What same sound do you hear in this list of words: let; peg; Ted? (/e/) (short e)	
-10- What same sound do you hear in this list of words: fish; slit; Liz? (/i/) (short i)	

Which Word Belongs? -4-	
Date: Student: Teacher:	
Skill Focus: CATEGORIZATION	**Correct = √**
Practice: *"Which of the following words does not belong: jump; jar; mar?"* (pause) *"mar"*	
-1- Which of the following words does not belong: seek; come; sand? (come)	
-2- Which of the following words does not belong: gear; give; Jake? (Jake)	
-3- Which of the following words does not belong: same; could; sip? (could)	
-4- Which of the following words does not belong: dock; light; lap? (dock)	
-5- Which of the following words does not belong: Mike; ship; bake? (ship)	
-6- Which of the following words does not belong: lack; tack; lunch? (lunch)	
-7- Which of the following words does not belong: face; tall; call? (face)	
-8- Which of the following words does not belong: bib; tip; jive? (jive)	
-9- Which of the following words does not belong: tan; clap; nose? (nose)	
-10- Which of the following words does not belong: tock; rip; lob? (rip)	

<table>
<tr><td colspan="2" align="center">**Word-Making Machine! -4-**</td></tr>
<tr><td colspan="2">Date: Student: Teacher:</td></tr>
<tr><td>**Skill Focus: BLENDING**</td><td>Correct = √</td></tr>
<tr><td colspan="2">**Practice: "What word can you make from putting together the following sounds: /p/ /a/ /t/?"** (pause) **"pat"**</td></tr>
<tr><td>-1- What word can you make from putting together the following sounds: /P/ /a/ /m/? (Pam)</td><td></td></tr>
<tr><td>-2- What word can you make from putting together the following sounds: /l/ /o/ /t/? (lot)</td><td></td></tr>
<tr><td>-3- What word can you make from putting together the following sounds: /b/ /e/ /d/? (bed)</td><td></td></tr>
<tr><td>-4- What word can you make from putting together the following sounds: /m/ /u/ /g/ /s/? (mugs)</td><td></td></tr>
<tr><td>-5- What word can you make from putting together the following sounds: /l/ /o/ /t/ /s/? (lots)</td><td></td></tr>
<tr><td>-6- What word can you make from putting together the following sounds: /s/ /l/ /i/ /p/? (slip)</td><td></td></tr>
<tr><td>-7- What word can you make from putting together the following sounds: /c/ /a/ /s/ /t/? (cast)</td><td></td></tr>
<tr><td>-8- What word can you make from putting together the following sounds: /s/ /a/ /k/ /r/ ? (saker)</td><td></td></tr>
<tr><td>-9- What word can you make from putting together the following sounds: /b/ /i/ /n/ /t/ /r/? (binter)</td><td></td></tr>
<tr><td>-10- What word can you make from putting together the following sounds: /l/ /u/ /p/ /r/? (lupper)</td><td></td></tr>
</table>

<table>
<tr><td colspan="2" align="center">**Sound Count! -4-**</td></tr>
<tr><td colspan="2">Date: Student: Teacher:</td></tr>
<tr><td>**Skill Focus: SEGMENTING**</td><td>Correct = √</td></tr>
<tr><td colspan="2">**Practice: "How many sounds do you hear in the following word? /h/ /a/ /t/?"** (pause) **"3"**</td></tr>
<tr><td>-1- How many sounds do you hear in the following word: /p /o/ /t/? (pot) (3)</td><td></td></tr>
<tr><td>-2- How many sounds do you hear in the following word: /e/ /m/? (em) (2)</td><td></td></tr>
<tr><td>-3- How many sounds do you hear in the following word: /t/ /i/ /p/? (tip) (3)</td><td></td></tr>
<tr><td>-4- How many sounds do you hear in the following word: /s/ /n/ /a/ /p/? (snap) (4)</td><td></td></tr>
<tr><td>-5- How many sounds do you hear in the following word: /c/ /l/ /i/ /p/? (clip) (4)</td><td></td></tr>
<tr><td>-6- How many sounds do you hear in the following word: /d/ /u/ /m/ /p/? (dump) (4)</td><td></td></tr>
<tr><td>-7- How many sounds do you hear in the following word: /p/ /u/ /n/ /t/? (punt) (4)</td><td></td></tr>
<tr><td>-8- How many sounds do you hear in the following word: /c/ /u/ /p/ /r/ /t/? (cuppert) (5)</td><td></td></tr>
<tr><td>-9- How many sounds do you hear in the following word: /f /a/ /k/ /r/? (faker) (4)</td><td></td></tr>
<tr><td>-10- How many sounds do you hear in the following word: /c /a/ /p/ /r/ /z/? (capers) (5)</td><td></td></tr>
</table>

Remove the Sound! -4-

Date: Student: Teacher:	
Skill Focus: MANIPULATION	Correct = √
Practice: *"Say car **without the /c/ at the beginning. You would say"** (pause) **"/r/."***	
-1- Say *lad* without the /l/. (ad)	
-2- Say *pit* without the /p/. (it)	
-3- Say *dot* without the /d/. (ot)	
-4- Say *skirt* without the /sk/. (irt)	
-5- Say *fast* without the /f/. (ast)	
-6- Say romp without the /r/. (omp)	
-7- Say *list* without the /l/. (ist)	
-8- Say *ast* with a /p/ at the beginning. (past)	
-9- Say *ap* with a /t/ at the beginning. (tap)	
-10- Say *last* with an /f/ instead of an /l/. (fast)	

Rhyming with Simple Words! -5-

Date: Student: Teacher:	
Skill Focus: RHYME	Correct = √
Practice: *"The two words that I am going to say may or may not rhyme, so listen carefully. Do lick and pick rhyme?"* (pause) *"Yes."*	
-1- Do wall and tall rhyme? (Yes)	
-2- Do sale and pale rhyme? (Yes)	
-3- Do lad and nip rhyme? (No)	
-4- Do back and crack rhyme? (Yes)	
-5- Do plan and name rhyme? (No)	
-6- Do trap and wrap rhyme? (Yes)	
-7- Do land and Mark rhyme? (No)	
-8- Do Frank and mound rhyme? (Yes)	
-9- Do swipe and claps rhyme? (No)	
-10- Do crasher and smasher rhyme? (Yes)	

Simple Sounds! -5-	
Date: Student: Teacher:	
Skill Focus: ALLITERATION	Correct = √
Practice: **"I am going to say three words: mouse; mate; might. Do all three words start with the same sound?"** (pause) **"Yes."**	
-1- (/d/) Do all three of these words start with the same sound: back; deer; bite? (No)	
-2- (/f/) Do all three of these words start with the same sound: fan; fight; fun? (Yes)	
-3- (/k/) Do all three of these words start with the same sound: care; come; cane? (Yes)	
-4- (/m/) Do all three of these words start with the same sound: nap; miss; note? (No)	
-5- (/bl/) Do all three of these words start with the same sound: bless; blab; blip? (Yes)	
-6- (/sl/) Do all three of these words start with the same sound: slid; sleuth; cloud? (No)	
-7- (/dr/) Do all three of these words start with the same sound: drape; dream; drive? (Yes)	
-8- (/ch/) Do all three of these words start with the same sound: chalk; chain; cheap? (Yes)	
-9- (/cr/) Do all three of these words start with the same sound: crack; smart; creep? (No)	
-10- (/sm/) Do all three of these words start with the same sound: scale; scope; scuba? (Yes)	

Word Count! -5-	
Date: Student: Teacher:	
Skill Focus: WORDS IN SENTENCES	Correct = √
Practice: **"How many words are in this list? The man laughed."** (pause) **"3"**	
-1- How many words are in this list? The tiny dog yapped. (4)	
-2- How many words are in this list? She swam fast. (3)	
-3- How many words are in this list? Jack and Todd raced. (4)	
-4- How many words are in this list? Our class is at recess. (5)	
-5- How many words are in this list? Dinner is ready now. (4)	
-6- How many words are in this list? The snake slithered away. (4)	
-7- How many words are in this list? Kathy walked to the office. (5)	
-8- How many words are in this list? The girls jumped in the water. (6)	
-9- How many words are in this list? Kenny's math test is tomorrow. (5)	
-10- How many words are in this list? Please listen when I am talking. (6)	

Gluing Words Together! -5-	
Date: Student: Teacher:	
Skill Focus: SYLLABLES	**Correct = √**
Practice: ***"Blend together the words that you hear (space; ship to spaceship), segment (butterfly to butter; fly), or remove a word (milkman without milk; man)."***	
-1- Listen to these two words: *ear; ache*. Say the entire word together. (earache)	
-2- Listen to these two words: *fire; man*. Say the entire word together. (fireman)	
-3- Listen to these two words: *ginger; bread*. Say the entire word together. (gingerbread)	
-4- Listen to these two words: *hard; ware*. Say the entire word together. (hardware)	
-5- What two words do you hear in *iceberg*? (ice; berg)	
-6- What two words do you hear in *kneecap*? (knee; cap)	
-7- What two words to you hear in *ladybug*? (lady; bug)	
-8- If you take *mail* out of *mailbox* what do you have left? (box)	
-9- If you take *gown* out of *nightgown* what do you have left? (night)	
-10- If you take *over* out of *overpaid* what do you have left? (paid)	

Use Your Glue Again—Beginning Sound to Ending Sound! -5-	
Date: Student: Teacher:	
Skill Focus: ONSET AND RIME	**Correct = √**
Practice: ***"Blend the following sounds: /t/-/ip/."*** (pause) ***"tip"***	
-1- Blend the following sounds: /f/-/ig/. (fig)	
-2- Blend the following sounds: /c/-/oat/. (coat)	
-3- Blend the following sounds: /b/-/urn/. (burn)	
-4- Blend the following sounds: /l/-/ock/. (lock)	
-5- Blend the following sounds: /sp/-/oon/. (spoon)	
-6- Blend the following sounds: /b/-/est/. (best)	
-7- Blend the following sounds: /sl/-/eep/. (sleep)	
-8- Blend the following sounds: /fr /-/oze/. (froze)	
-9- Blend the following sounds: /bl/-/ess/. (bless)	
-10- Blend the following sounds: /cr/-/ash/. (crash)	

Find the Sound! -5-	
Date: Student: Teacher:	
Skill Focus: ISOLATION	Correct = √
Practice: "What sound do you hear at the beginning of tock; tear; tan?" (pause) **"/t/"** (sound, not letter)	
-1- What do you hear at the **beginning** of door; deck; dip? (/d/)	
-2- What do you hear at the **beginning** of post; pear; pick? (/p/)	
-3- What do you hear at the **beginning** of knit; note; knack? (/n/)	
-4- What do you hear at the **beginning** of Sue; sight; sand? (/s/)	
-5- What do you hear at the **end** of walk; stalk; milk? (/k/)	
-6- What do you hear at the **end** of sky; fly; try? (/i/) (long i)	
-7- What do you hear at the **end** of bold; road; dead? (/d/)	
-8- What do you hear in the **middle** of take; mate; dame? (/a/) (long a)	
-9- What do you hear in the **middle** of lid; pit; kiss? (/i/)	
-10- What do you hear in the **middle** of sass; tap; back? (/a/)	

Find the Same Sound! -5-	
Date: Student: Teacher:	
Skill Focus: IDENTITY	Correct = √
Practice: "What same sound do you hear in this list of words: lip; lean; lad?" (pause) **"/l/"** (sound, not letter)	
-1- What same sound do you hear in this list of words: igloo; inch; is? (/i/)	
-2- What same sound do you hear in this list of words: ate; ace; acorn? (/a/) (long a)	
-3- What same sound do you hear in this list of words: must; mop; mate? (/m/)	
-4- What same sound do you hear in this list of words: turn; take; tile? (/t/)	
-5- What same sound do you hear in this list of words: rain; pawn; down? (/n/)	
-6- What same sound do you hear in this list of words: miss; those; crass? (/s/)	
-7- What same sound do you hear in this list of words: city; bitty; lucky? (/e/) (long e)	
-8- What same sound do you hear in this list of words: tap; mad; laugh? (/a/) (short a)	
-9- What same sound do you hear in this list of words: met; leg; Ted? (/e/) (short e)	
-10- What same sound do you hear in this list of words: wish; pit; lip? (/i/) (short i)	

Which Word Belongs? -5-	
Date: Student: Teacher:	
Skill Focus: CATEGORIZATION	Correct = √
Practice: *"Which of the following words does not belong: pump; park; miss?"* (pause) *"miss"*	
-1- Which of the following words does not belong: soar; care; send? (care)	
-2- Which of the following words does not belong: just; jive; gift? (gift)	
-3- Which of the following words does not belong: ice; easy; enough? (ice)	
-4- Which of the following words does not belong: bark; door; bite? (door)	
-5- Which of the following words does not belong: make; shed; bake? (shed)	
-6- Which of the following words does not belong: flack; pack; bunch? (bunch)	
-7- Which of the following words does not belong: place; wall; mall? (place)	
-8- Which of the following words does not belong: rude; tune; mate? (mate)	
-9- Which of the following words does not belong: book; took; rose? (rose)	
-10- Which of the following words does not belong: blob; rain; sock? (rain)	

Word-Making Machine! -5-	
Date: Student: Teacher:	
Skill Focus: BLENDING	Correct = √
Practice: *"What word can you make from putting together the following sounds: /s/ /a/ /t/?"* (pause) *"sat"*	
-1- What word can you make from putting together the following sounds: /h/ /i/ /t/? (hit)	
-2- What word can you make from putting together the following sounds: /m/ /a/ /d/? (lot)	
-3- What word can you make from putting together the following sounds: /T/ /e/ /d/? (Ted)	
-4- What word can you make from putting together the following sounds: /l/ /u/ /g/ /s/? (lugs)	
-5- What word can you make from putting together the following sounds: /c/ /a/ /p/ /s/? (caps)	
-6- What word can you make from putting together the following sounds: /s/ /l/ /e/ /d/? (sled)	
-7- What word can you make from putting together the following sounds: /m/ /a/ /s/ /t/? (mast)	
-8- What word can you make from putting together the following sounds: /l/ /a/ /k/ /r/ ? (laker)	
-9- What word can you make from putting together the following sounds: /k/ /i/ /n/ /t/ /r/? (kinter)	
-10- What word can you make from putting together the following sounds: /b/ /u/ /p/ /r/? (bupper)	

Sound Count! -5-	
Date: Student: Teacher:	
Skill Focus: SEGMENTING	Correct = √
Practice: *"How many sounds do you hear in the following word? /h/ /a/ /t/?"* (pause) *"3"*	
-1- How many sounds do you hear in the following word: /l /0/ /t/? (lot) (3)	
-2- How many sounds do you hear in the following word: /u/ /s/? (us) (2)	
-3- How many sounds do you hear in the following word: /d/ /i/ /p/? (dip) (3)	
-4- How many sounds do you hear in the following word: /s/ /l/ /i/ /p/? (slip) (4)	
-5- How many sounds do you hear in the following word: /c/ /l/ /o/ /p/? (clop) (4)	
-6- How many sounds do you hear in the following word: /r/ /a/ /k/? (rack) (3)	
-7- How many sounds do you hear in the following word: /h/ /u/ /n/ /t/? (hunt) (4)	
-8- How many sounds do you hear in the following word: /l/ /u/ /p/ /r/ /t/? (luppert) (5)	
-9- How many sounds do you hear in the following word: /d /a/ /k/ /r/? (daker) (4)	
-10- How many sounds do you hear in the following word: /z /a/ /p/ /r/ /z/? (zapers) (5)	

Remove the Sound! -5-	
Date: Student: Teacher:	
Skill Focus: MANIPULATION	Correct = √
Practice: *"Say car without the /c/ at the beginning. You would say"* (pause) *"/r/."*	
-1- Say *sky* without the /s/. (ky)	
-2- Say *rain* without the /r/. (ain)	
-3- Say *dry* without the /d/. (ry)	
-4- Say *skid* without the /sk/. (id)	
-5- Say *post* without the /p/. (ost)	
-6- Say stop without the /s/. (top)	
-7- Say *tent* without the /t/. (ent)	
-8- Say *eal* with an /s/ at the beginning. (seal)	
-9- Say ack with an /sn/ at the beginning. (snack)	
-10- Say *ave* with a /c/ at the beginning. (cave)	

Rhyming with Simple Words! -6-	
Date: Student: Teacher:	
Skill Focus: RHYME	Correct = √
Practice: "*The two words that I am going to say may or may not rhyme, so listen carefully. Do tap and lap rhyme*?" (pause) *"Yes."*	
-1- Do wail and tail rhyme? (Yes)	
-2- Do rage and cage rhyme? (Yes)	
-3- Do sad and can rhyme? (No)	
-4- Do plain and rain rhyme? (Yes)	
-5- Do plant and lame rhyme? (No)	
-6- Do shake and break rhyme? (Yes)	
-7- Do hand and led rhyme? (No)	
-8- Do tame and frame rhyme? (Yes)	
-9- Do shrank and snap rhyme? (No)	
-10- Do cram and exam rhyme? (Yes)	

Simple Sounds! -6-	
Date: Student: Teacher:	
Skill Focus: ALLITERATION	Correct = √
Practice: *"I am going to say three words: mitt; mat; mud. Do all three words start with the same sound?"* (pause) *"Yes."*	
-1- (/d/) Do all three of these words start with the same sound: does; big; dip? (No)	
-2- (/f/) Do all three of these words start with the same sound: bull; bear; bad? (Yes)	
-3- (/k/) Do all three of these words start with the same sound: cat; cone; cap? (Yes)	
-4- (/m/) Do all three of these words start with the same sound: nod; mist; nap? (No)	
-5- (/bl/) Do all three of these words start with the same sound: blot; black; bleed? (Yes)	
-6- (/sl/) Do all three of these words start with the same sound: slave; slob; clout? (No)	
-7- (/dr/) Do all three of these words start with the same sound: dread; drape; drill? (Yes)	
-8- (/ch/) Do all three of these words start with the same sound: clench; clip; clog? (Yes)	
-9- (/cr/) Do all three of these words start with the same sound: craft; street; crook? (No)	
-10- (/sm/) Do all three of these words start with the same sound: spread; sprint; spray? (Yes)	

Word Count! -6-	
Date: Student: Teacher:	
Skill Focus: WORDS IN SENTENCES	Correct = √
Practice: **"How many words are in this list? The phone rang.**" (pause) **"3"**	
-1- How many words are in this list? I am so sad. (4)	
-2- How many words are in this list? John went home. (3)	
-3- How many words are in this list? She was sick yesterday. (4)	
-4- How many words are in this list? Linda went over there. (4)	
-5- How many words are in this list? I am ready for summer. (5)	
-6- How many words are in this list? The monkey ate a banana. (5)	
-7- How many words are in this list? Drew jumped on the couch. (5)	
-8- How many words are in this list? Our class walked to the playground. (6)	
-9- How many words are in this list? They washed and folded the clothes. (6)	
-10- How many words are in this list? Please stop that right now. (5)	

Gluing Words Together! -6-	
Date: Student: Teacher:	
Skill Focus: SYLLABLES	Correct = √
Practice: Practice Item: **"Blend together the words that you hear (window; pane to windowpane), segment (bathroom to bath; room), or remove a word (footrest without foot; rest)."**	
-1- Listen to these two words: *neck; tie*. Say the entire word together. (necktie)	
-2- Listen to these two words: *over; due*. Say the entire word together. (overdue)	
-3- Listen to these two words: *milk; shake*. Say the entire word together. (milkshake)	
-4- Listen to these two words: *market; place*. Say the entire word together. (marketplace)	
-5- What two words do you hear in *newborn*? (new; born)	
-6- What two words do you hear in *postcard*? (post; card)	
-7- What two words to you hear in *overnight*? (over; night)	
-8- If you take *scare* out of *scarecrow* what do you have left? (crow)	
-9- If you take *bud* out of *rosebud* what do you have left? (rose)	
-10- If you take *sea* out of *seaweed* what do you have left? (weed)	

Use Your Glue Again—Beginning Sound to Ending Sound! -6-	
Date: Student: Teacher:	
Skill Focus: ONSET AND RIME	Correct = √
Practice: *"Blend the following sounds: /t/-/ug/."* (pause) *"tug"*	
-1- Blend the following sounds: /f/-/ig/. (fig)	
-2- Blend the following sounds: /p/-/et/. (pet)	
-3- Blend the following sounds: /f/-/ern/. (fern)	
-4- Blend the following sounds: /bl/-/ock/. (block)	
-5- Blend the following sounds: /sp/-/are/. (spare)	
-6- Blend the following sounds: /b/-/ash/. (bash)	
-7- Blend the following sounds: /sh/-/out/. (shout)	
-8- Blend the following sounds: /fr /-/om/. (from)	
-9- Blend the following sounds: /bl/-/aze/. (blaze)	
-10- Blend the following sounds: /cr/-/uise/. (cruise)	

Find the Sound! -6-	
Date: Student: Teacher:	
Skill Focus: ISOLATION	Correct = √
Practice: *"What sound do you hear at the beginning of cut; camp; care?"* (pause) *"/c/"* (sound, not letter)	
-1- What do you hear at the **beginning** of free; flip; font? (/f/)	
-2- What do you hear at the **beginning** of tip; tear; tack? (/t/)	
-3- What do you hear at the **beginning** of know; not; now? (/n/)	
-4- What do you hear at the **beginning** of saw; sip; suds? (/s/)	
-5- What do you hear at the **end** of wait; might; tot? (/t/)	
-6- What do you hear at the **end** of roar; dear; fur? (/r/)	
-7- What do you hear at the **end** of mold; toad; head? (/d/)	
-8- What do you hear in the **middle** of flip; lid; tick? (/i/)	
-9- What do you hear in the **middle** of fun; mud; cut? (/u/)	
-10- What do you hear in the **middle** of peg; bed; let? (/e/)	

Find the Same Sound! -6-	
Date: Student: Teacher:	
Skill Focus: IDENTITY	Correct = √
Practice: *"What same sound do you hear in this list of words: book; bar; burn?"* (pause) *"/b/"* (sound, not letter)	
-1- What same sound do you hear in this list of words: under; umbrella; us? (/u/)	
-2- What same sound do you hear in this list of words: cash; cob; cut? (/c/)	
-3- What same sound do you hear in this list of words: make; mitt; must? (/m/)	
-4- What same sound do you hear in this list of words: tip; tail; tuck? (/t/)	
-5- What same sound do you hear in this list of words: pain; fawn; clown? (/n/)	
-6- What same sound do you hear in this list of words: hiss; close; grass? (/s/)	
-7- What same sound do you hear in this list of words: leg; bet; red? (/e/) (short e)	
-8- What same sound do you hear in this list of words: lap; tad; sat? (/a/) (short a)	
-9- What same sound do you hear in this list of words: fun; mud; putt? (/u/) (short u)	
-10- What same sound do you hear in this list of words: jog; gob; trot? (/O/) (short o)	

Which Word Belongs? -6-	
Date: Student: Teacher:	
Skill Focus: CATEGORIZATION	Correct = √
Practice: *"Which of the following words does not belong: pump; pick; made?"* (pause) *"made"*	
-1- Which of the following words does not belong: came; card; sit? (sit)	
-2- Which of the following words does not belong: gave; gar; just? (just)	
-3- Which of the following words does not belong: dart; door; bat? (bat)	
-4- Which of the following words does not belong: bust; den; bark? (bark)	
-5- Which of the following words does not belong: flake; slap; Blake? (slap)	
-6- Which of the following words does not belong: lunch; bunch; have? (have)	
-7- Which of the following words does not belong: face; tall; crawl? (face)	
-8- Which of the following words does not belong: nice; gate; mate? (nice)	
-9- Which of the following words does not belong: look; shook; toes? (toes)	
-10- Which of the following words does not belong: tock; rock; plop? (plop)	

Word-Making Machine! -6-	
Date: Student: Teacher:	
Skill Focus: BLENDING	Correct = √
Practice: ***"What word can you make from putting together the following sounds: /l/ /a/ /d/?"*** (pause) ***"lad"***	
-1- What word can you make from putting together the following sounds: /r/ /a/ /c/ /k/? (rack)	
-2- What word can you make from putting together the following sounds: /s/ /i/ /p/? (sip)	
-3- What word can you make from putting together the following sounds: /l/ /a/ /ck/? (lack)	
-4- What word can you make from putting together the following sounds: /t/ /e/ /n/ /d/? (tend)	
-5- What word can you make from putting together the following sounds: /b/ /a/ /p/ /s/? (baps)	
-6- What word can you make from putting together the following sounds: /s/ /l/ /i/ /p/? (slip)	
-7- What word can you make from putting together the following sounds: /c/ /a/ /s/ /t/? (cast)	
-8- What word can you make from putting together the following sounds: /c/ /a/ /k/ /r/ ? (caker)	
-9- What word can you make from putting together the following sounds: /spl/ /i/ /n/ /t/ /r/? (splinter)	
-10- What word can you make from putting together the following sounds: /cr/ /a/ /sh/? (crash)	

Sound Count! -6-	
Date: Student: Teacher:	
Skill Focus: SEGMENTING	Correct = √
Practice: ***"How many sounds do you hear in the following word? /l/ /i/ /p/?"*** (pause) ***"3"***	
-1- How many sounds do you hear in the following word: /m /0/ /p/? (mop) (3)	
-2- How many sounds do you hear in the following word: / S/ /a/ /m/? (Sam) (3)	
-3- How many sounds do you hear in the following word: /a/ /t/? (at) (2)	
-4- How many sounds do you hear in the following word: /b/ /o/ /x/? (box) (3)	
-5- How many sounds do you hear in the following word: /f/ /l/ /o/ /p/? (flop) (4)	
-6- How many sounds do you hear in the following word: /t/ /a/ /k/? (tack) (3)	
-7- How many sounds do you hear in the following word: /j/ /u/ /m/ /p/? (jump) (4)	
-8- How many sounds do you hear in the following word: /st/ /o/ /p/? (stop) (4)	
-9- How many sounds do you hear in the following word: /gl/ /a/ /s/? (glass) (4)	
-10- How many sounds do you hear in the following word: /n /a/ /p/ /k/ /i/ /n/? (napkin) (6)	

Remove the Sound! -6-	
Date: Student: Teacher:	
Skill Focus: MANIPULATION	Correct = √
Practice: **"Say tar _without the /t/ at the beginning. You would say"_** (pause) **_"/r/."_**	
-1- Say _try_ without the /t/. (ry)	
-2- Say _pain_ without the /p/. (ain)	
-3- Say _fly_ without the /f/. (ly)	
-4- Say _trip_ without the /tr/. (ip)	
-5- Say _most_ without the /m/. (ost)	
-6- Say _step_ without the /st/. (ep)	
-7- Say _mint_ without the /m/. (int)	
-8- Say _ail_ with an /s/ at the beginning. (sail)	
-9- Say _ack_ with a /p/ at the beginning. (pack)	
-10- Say _ave_ with an /h/ at the beginning. (have)	

Rhyming with Simple Words! -7-	
Date: Student: Teacher:	
Skill Focus: RHYME	Correct = √
Practice: **_"The two words that I am going to say may or may not rhyme, so listen carefully. Do lot and pot rhyme?"_** (pause) **_"Yes."_**	
-1- Do tall and fall rhyme? (Yes)	
-2- Do age and sage rhyme? (Yes)	
-3- Do mad and tan rhyme? (No)	
-4- Do flip and slip rhyme? (Yes)	
-5- Do choose and ladder rhyme? (No)	
-6- Do bread and head rhyme? (Yes)	
-7- Do land and race rhyme? (No)	
-8- Do face and pace rhyme? (Yes)	
-9- Do shoe and house rhyme? (No)	
-10- Do zipper and lipper rhyme? (Yes)	

Simple Sounds! -7-	
Date: Student: Teacher:	
Skill Focus: ALLITERATION	Correct = √
Practice: *"I am going to say three words: miss; map; much. Do all three words start with the same sound?"* (pause) *"Yes."*	
-1- (/d/) Do all three of these words start with the same sound: dear; bug; dog? (No)	
-2- (/f/) Do all three of these words start with the same sound: after; apple; ask? (Yes)	
-3- (/k/) Do all three of these words start with the same sound: cut; cape; cat? (Yes)	
-4- (/m/) Do all three of these words start with the same sound: make; note; must? (No)	
-5- (/bl/) Do all three of these words start with the same sound: bland; bless; blue? (Yes)	
-6- (/sl/) Do all three of these words start with the same sound: sleep; slap; cloud? (No)	
-7- (/dr/) Do all three of these words start with the same sound: draw; drop; dress? (Yes)	
-8- (/ch/) Do all three of these words start with the same sound: clap; clue; club? (Yes)	
-9- (/cr/) Do all three of these words start with the same sound: strange; strap; craze? (No)	
-10- (/sm/) Do all three of these words start with the same sound: sneeze; snip; snuff? (Yes)	

Word Count! -7-	
Date: Student: Teacher:	
Skill Focus: WORDS IN SENTENCES	Correct = √
Practice: *"How many words are in this list? The bird chirped."* (pause) *"3"*	
-1- How many words are in this list? I am so glad. (4)	
-2- How many words are in this list? Anna went home. (3)	
-3- How many words are in this list? He walked to school. (4)	
-4- How many words are in this list? Dave went to work. (4)	
-5- How many words are in this list? The wind howled loudly. (4)	
-6- How many words are in this list? The boys laughed and played. (5)	
-7- How many words are in this list? They jumped on the bed. (5)	
-8- How many words are in this list? The horse galloped across the field. (6)	
-9- How many words are in this list? Sam and Susan washed the car. (6)	
-10- How many words are in this list? Please do not run inside. (5)	

Gluing Words Together! -7-

Date: Student: Teacher:	

Skill Focus: SYLLABLES	Correct = √
Practice: "Blend together the words that you hear (bird; house to birdhouse), segment (waterpark to water; park), or remove a word (handshake without hand; shake)."	
-1- Listen to these two words: *earth; quake*. Say the entire word together. (earthquake)	
-2- Listen to these two words: *grass; hopper*. Say the entire word together. (grasshopper)	
-3- Listen to these two words: *sun; flower*. Say the entire word together. (sunflower)	
-4- Listen to these two words: *weather; man*. Say the entire word together. (weatherman)	
-5- What two words do you hear in *moonlight*? (moon; light)	
-6- What two words do you hear in *lighthouse*? (light; house)	
-7- What two words to you hear in *overcome*? (over; come)	
-8- If you take *boat* out of *boathouse* what do you have left? (house)	
-9- If you take *noon* out of *afternoon* what do you have left? (after)	
-10- If you take *night* out of *nighttime* what do you have left? (time)	

Use Your Glue Again—Beginning Sound to Ending Sound! -7-

Date: Student: Teacher:	

Skill Focus: ONSET AND RIME	Correct = √
Practice: "Blend the following sounds: /fl/-/ip/." (pause) **"flip"**	
-1- Blend the following sounds: /b/-/ug/. (bug)	
-2- Blend the following sounds: /s/-/et/. (set)	
-3- Blend the following sounds: /l/-/ean/. (lean)	
-4- Blend the following sounds: /bl/-/ot/. (blot)	
-5- Blend the following sounds: /sp/-/ace/. (space)	
-6- Blend the following sounds: /cl/-/oud/. (cloud)	
-7- Blend the following sounds: /sh/-/ed/. (shed)	
-8- Blend the following sounds: /fr /-/oze/. (froze)	
-9- Blend the following sounds: /bl/-/ame/. (blame)	
-10- Blend the following sounds: /cr/-/eam/. (cream)	

Find the Sound! -7-	
Date: Student: Teacher:	
Skill Focus: ISOLATION	**Correct = √**
Practice: ***"What sound do you hear at the beginning of pop; pick; pad?"*** (pause) ***"/p/"*** (sound, not letter)	
-1- What do you hear at the **beginning** of bat; big; buzz? (/b/)	
-2- What do you hear at the **beginning** of tap; toe; tick? (/t/)	
-3- What do you hear at the **beginning** of car; cup; cob? (/c/)	
-4- What do you hear at the **beginning** of sap; sick; supper? (/s/)	
-5- What do you hear at the **end** of late; right; pot? (/t/)	
-6- What do you hear at the **end** of pig; bag; lug? (/r/)	
-7- What do you hear at the **end** of lack; tick; pock? (/k/)	
-8- What do you hear in the **middle** of lip; big; Rick? (/i/)	
-9- What do you hear in the **middle** of run; mutt; cut? (/u/)	
-10- What do you hear in the **middle** of leg; Ted; met? (/e/)	

Find the Same Sound! -7-	
Date: Student: Teacher:	
Skill Focus: IDENTITY	**Correct = √**
Practice: ***"What same sound do you hear in this list of words: bark; big; bust?"*** (pause) ***"/b/"*** (sound, not letter)	
-1- What same sound do you hear in this list of words: use; unit; uniform? (/u/) (long u)	
-2- What same sound do you hear in this list of words: cap; cob; cut? (/c/)	
-3- What same sound do you hear in this list of words: mash; mop; mutt? (/m/)	
-4- What same sound do you hear in this list of words: tock; tame; ten? (/t/)	
-5- What same sound do you hear in this list of words: rain; lawn; frown? (/n/)	
-6- What same sound do you hear in this list of words: kiss; rose; glass? (/s/)	
-7- What same sound do you hear in this list of words: peg; red; met? (/e/) (short e)	
-8- What same sound do you hear in this list of words: pap; lad; sat? (/a/) (short a)	
-9- What same sound do you hear in this list of words: tone; rode; home? (/o/) (long o)	
-10- What same sound do you hear in this list of words: bog; pot; lob? (/O/) (short o)	

Which Word Belongs? -7-

Date: Student: Teacher:	
Skill Focus: CATEGORIZATION	Correct = √
Practice: *"Which of the following words does not belong: egg; elephant; ice?"* (pause) *"ice"*	
-1- Which of the following words does not belong: city; sand; come? (come)	
-2- Which of the following words does not belong: just; jar; gave? (gave)	
-3- Which of the following words does not belong: bat; bend; door? (door)	
-4- Which of the following words does not belong: dip; den; back? (back)	
-5- Which of the following words does not belong: make; lap; cave? (lap)	
-6- Which of the following words does not belong: crunch; bunch; tube? (tube)	
-7- Which of the following words does not belong: lace; wall; crawl? (lace)	
-8- Which of the following words does not belong: mice; gate; crate? (mice)	
-9- Which of the following words does not belong: took; shook; goes? (goes)	
-10- Which of the following words does not belong: back; lack; make? (make)	

Word-Making Machine! -7-

Date: Student: Teacher:	
Skill Focus: BLENDING	Correct = √
Practice: *"What word can you make from putting together the following sounds: /p/ /o/ /p/?"* (pause) *"pop"*	
-1- What word can you make from putting together the following sounds: /p/ /a/ /c/ /k/? (pack)	
-2- What word can you make from putting together the following sounds: /z/ /i/ /p/? (zip)	
-3- What word can you make from putting together the following sounds: /l/ /i/ /ck/? (lick)	
-4- What word can you make from putting together the following sounds: /s/ /e/ /n/ /d/? (send)	
-5- What word can you make from putting together the following sounds: /t/ /a/ /p/ /s/? (taps)	
-6- What word can you make from putting together the following sounds: /s/ /l/ /e/ /d/? (sled)	
-7- What word can you make from putting together the following sounds: /f/ /a/ /s/ /t/? (fast)	
-8- What word can you make from putting together the following sounds: /b/ /a/ /k/ /r/? (baker)	
-9- What word can you make from putting together the following sounds: /bl/ /e/ /n/ /d/ /r/? (blender)	
-10- What word can you make from putting together the following sounds: /cr/ /a/ /b/? (crab)	

Sound Count! -7-	
Date: Student: Teacher:	
Skill Focus: SEGMENTING	Correct = √
Practice: *"How many sounds do you hear in the following word? /h/ /u/ /t/?"* (pause) *"3"*	
-1- How many sounds do you hear in the following word: /m /a/ /d/? (mad) (3)	
-2- How many sounds do you hear in the following word: / P/ /a/ /m/? (Pam) (3)	
-3- How many sounds do you hear in the following word: /u/ /s/? (us) (2)	
-4- How many sounds do you hear in the following word: /f/ /o/ /x/? (fox) (3)	
-5- How many sounds do you hear in the following word: /f/ /l/ /o/ /t/? (float) (4)	
-6- How many sounds do you hear in the following word: /r/ /a/ /k/? (rack) (3)	
-7- How many sounds do you hear in the following word: /b/ /u/ /m/ /p/? (bump) (4)	
-8- How many sounds do you hear in the following word: /st/ /a/ n/ /d/? (stand) (4)	
-9- How many sounds do you hear in the following word: /gl/ /a/ /z/? (glaze) (4)	
-10- How many sounds do you hear in the following word: /tr /a/ /f/ /i/ /c/? (traffic) (5)	

Remove the Sound! -7-	
Date: Student: Teacher:	
Skill Focus: MANIPULATION	Correct = √
Practice: *"Say park without the /p/ at the beginning. You would say"* (pause) *"/ark/."*	
-1- Say *pry* without the /p/. (ry)	
-2- Say *rain* without the /r/. (ain)	
-3- Say *sly* without the /s/. (ly)	
-4- Say *tree* without the /tr/. (ee)	
-5- Say *lost* without the /l/. (ost)	
-6- Say *stood* without the /st/. (ood)	
-7- Say *lint* without the /l/. (int)	
-8- Say *ail* with a /p/ at the beginning. (pail)	
-9- Say *ack* with an /s/ at the beginning. (sack)	
-10- Say *ave* with a /g/ at the beginning. (gave)	

PLAYING WITH WORD FORMS

Assess and Then Teach! Directions for Assessment of Word Parts

The Morphology Assessment is administered individually to students by the evaluator. The assessment is made up of five sections with ten items per page and ten versions of each section. The sections have brief directions and a test practice item. The evaluator will begin with the practice item and make sure the student knows what is expected of him or her. After making sure the student understands the practice item, the evaluator will read the test items to the student, wait for a response, and then place a check mark by each item that is answered correctly. If the student misses half or more of the test items on that page, that section of testing is over, and the next one begins. Continue with this process until all five sections have been scored.

WORD PART ASSESSMENT

Morphological—Word Parts That Change the Meaning of a Word

The five sections are Build the Word with Patterns!, Word Part Remover!, Gluing Word Parts!, Finish the Sentence!, and Word Play! Below you will see directions for each section.

Build the Word with Patterns! There is a set of four words by each number. The evaluator should repeat the first three words clearly and distinctively, then wait for the student to give the final word. The answer is in boldfaced type. If the student answers correctly, place a check mark in the box to the right of the test item.

Word Part Remover! Read the pseudo word for each item and wait for the student to give you the shortened version of the pseudo word that has had the affixes removed. The answer is in boldfaced type. Mark the correct responses with a check mark in the box on the right. Again, the test section continues until the student has missed half or more of the test items on that page. When that number has been reached, move to the next section.

Gluing Word Parts! The evaluator will slowly say the parts of the word, and the student will repeat the parts. The student then combines the parts to make a real word or pseudo word. The answers are in parentheses at the end of the item line. Mark the correct responses in the boxes, to the right. Stop this section when half or more of the items are missed. Then move to the next section.

Finish the Sentence! The evaluator will read the first two sentences, the first sentence of the next set, and then part of the next sentence, waiting for the student to complete it. The student should give you the answer that is in boldfaced type at the end of the test item. Mark the correct responses with a check mark in the box and continue until half or more items are missed in this section. Move to the next section and begin.

Word Play! The evaluator will read the sentence containing pseudo words with real affixes for the student. The student will tell what the sentence means by using the prefix meanings. The student should offer a negative response. Mark the correct responses with a check mark in the box and continue until half or more items are missed in this section.

Build the Word with Patterns!—Section 1 -v1-	
Date: Student: Teacher:	
Skill Focus: Affixation	**Correct = √**

Directions for Build the Word with Patterns: Slowly repeat the first two words, pause, then say the third word. Ask the student to supply the final word to complete the set. The answer is in bold for each item. Mark the correct response with a check mark in the box. Be sure to use the practice item first to help the student understand what is expected. Begin the test and continue until the student misses half or more of the items on the page, then move to the next section.

Practice: *"Listen:* gush: gushed. *Listen again:* tush. *What is next?"* (**tushed**)

-1- mesh: meshed—besh: **beshed**	
-2- ram: rams—bim: **bims**	
-3- bake: baking—sake: **saking**	
-4- mop: mopper—fop: **fopper**	
-5- catch: catcher—gatch: **gatcher**	
-6- bats: bat—dats: **dat**	
-7- honor: dishonor—continue: **discontinue**	
-8- unreal: real—just: **unjust**	
-9- plain: plainly—bate: **bately**	
-10- music: musician—fusic: **fuscian**	

Word Part Remover!—Section 2 -v1-	
Date: Student: Teacher:	
Skill Focus: Affix Deletion	**Correct = √**

Directions for Word Part Remover: Read the pseudo word for each item and wait for the student to give you the shortened version of the pseudo word that has had the affixes removed. The answer is in bold. Mark the correct responses with a check mark in the box on the right. Continue until the student has missed half or more of the test items on the page, then move to the next section.

Practice: *"Repeat:* binking. *Remove the affix and say the shortened word."* (**bink**)

-1- zins: **zin**	
-2- zilled: **zill**	
-3- dacking: **dack**	
-4- zainly: **zain**	
-5- fetter: **fet**	
-6- macked: **mack**	
-7- lishes: **lish**	
-8- dunning: **dun**	
-9- maver: **mave**	
-10- taction: **tact**	

Gluing Word Parts!—Section 3 -v1-

Date: Student: Teacher:

Skill Focus: Combining Word Parts	Correct = √

Directions for Gluing Word Parts: The evaluator will slowly say the parts of the word, and the student will repeat the parts. Then the student combines the parts to make a real word or pseudo word. The answers are in parentheses at the end of the item line. Mark the correct responses in the boxes to the right. Stop when half or more of the items are missed, then move to the next section.

Practice: "Repeat after me: 're' + 'do.' Combined it is **(redo)**."

-1- "Repeat after me: 're' + 'shape.' Combined it is **(reshape)**."	
-2- "Repeat after me: 'un' + 'happy.' Combined it is **(unhappy)**."	
-3- "Repeat after me: 'in' + 'visible.' Combined it is **(invisible)**."	
-4- "Repeat after me: 'dis' + 'able.' Combined it is **(disable)**."	
-5- "Repeat after me: 'pre' + 'treat.' Combined it is **(pretreat)**."	
-6- "Repeat after me: 'mis' + 'trust.' Combined it is **(mistrust)**."	
-7- "Repeat after me: 'trust' + 'ing.' Combined it is **(trusting)**."	
-8- "Repeat after me: 'help' + 'less.' Combined it is **(helpless)**."	
-9- "Repeat after me: 'rest' + 'ful.' Combined it is **(restful)**."	
-10-"Repeat after me: 'ex' + 'port' + 'er.' Combined it is **(exporter)**."	

Finish the Sentence!—Section 4 -v1-

Date: Student: Teacher:

Skill Focus: Morpheme Pattern Match	Correct = √

Directions for Finish the Sentence: The evaluator will read the first two sentences, the first sentence of the next set, and then part of the next sentence, waiting for the student to complete it. The student should give you the answer that is in bold in the last sentence. Mark the correct responses in the boxes to the right. Stop when half or more of the items are missed, then move to the next section.

Practice: "Listen to the first two sentences. Now listen again and see if you can finish the sentence when I stop. 'The jogger jogs: The speeder speeds.' 'The shopper shops: The singer *sings*.'"

-1-.The baby wet his diaper: The baby wets his diaper. The man put the paper down: The man **puts** the paper down.	
-2- Rita talked to Dale: Rita talks to Dale. Sophie laughed at the kitten: Sophie **laughs** at the kitten.	
-3- Bob was marked: Bob was unmarked. Sally was zacked: Sally was **unzacked.**	
-4- The robber robs: The scrubber scrubs. The hugger hugs: The digger **digs**.	
-5- The man covered the grill: The man covers the grill. The man cleaned the pool: The man **cleans** the pool.	
-6- Ron's car is fancy: Dak's car is fancier. Tameka is pretty: Simone is **prettier**.	
-7- Martha clears the walkway: Martha is clearing the walkway. Phil bangs the door: Phil is **banging** the door.	
-8- The salt is salty: The grit is gritty. The butter is buttery: The cream is **creamy**.	
-9- Meg is unwilling to work: Meg can be very unwillingly to work. The lady is unkind: The lady is behaving **unkindly**.	
-10- Lee's dog had matched eyes: Ray's dog had mismatched eyes. The boy learned the math equation: The girl **mislearned** the math equation.	

Word Play!—Section 5 -v1-	
Date: Student: Teacher:	
Skill Focus: Define Pseudo Words	Correct = √

Directions for Word Play: The evaluator will read the sentence containing pseudo words with real affixes. The student will tell what the sentence means by using the prefix meanings and offer a negative response. The answer is in bold at the end of the item. Mark the correct responses in the boxes to the right. Stop when half or more of the items are missed, then move to the next section.

Practice: *"Listen as I read the sentence that has a made-up word and tell me what it means. 'The clown depainted his face, since he already had a big smile.'"* **(clown did not paint his face, because he had a big smile)**

-1- Ricky was new in the school and was nonfriended. **(no friends because he was new)**	
-2- Cindy unwalks her dog every day, since her friend helps. **(does not walk dog every day because friend helps)**	
-3- Lizards declimbed, only, on the tree branch. **(lizards did not climb only on tree branch)**	
-4- Jeri unfavored the second movie over the first one. **(did not like second movie the most)**	
-5- The computer game was fun to play, but it was depowered. **(liked to play game, but not powered)**	
-6- Snow skiing is fun while falling is disfun. **(sun skiing fun, falling is not)**	
-7- The red team unwon the baseball game. **(red team did not win game)**	
-8- Michael wanted to go swimming, but the lifeguard was unworking. **(wanted to swim, but no lifeguard)**	
-9- Baxter and Casey dewalked the mountain trail, because of the snow. **(did not walk trail because of snow)**	
-10- Aunt Cathy's chicken was disfried. **(chicken not fried)**	

Build the Word with Patterns!—Section 1 -v2-	
Date: Student: Teacher:	
Skill Focus: Affixation	**Correct = √**
Directions for Build the Word with Patterns: Slowly repeat the first two words, pause, then say the third word. Ask the student to supply the final word to complete the set. The answer is in bold for each item. Mark the correct response with a check mark in the box. Be sure to use the practice item first to help the student understand what is expected. Begin the test and continue until the student misses half or more of the items on the page, then move to the next section.	
Practice: *"Listen:* gush: gushed. *Listen again:* tush. *What is next?"* (**tushed**)	
-1- mike: miked—pike: **piked**	
-2- jump: jumps—hamp: **hamps**	
-3- lace: lacing—dace: **dacing**	
-4- bag: bagger—mag: **magger**	
-5- pack: packer—dack: **dacker**	
-6- sits: sit—vits: **vit**	
-7- connect: disconnect— like: **dislike**	
-8- unnecessary: necessary—developed: **undeveloped**	
-9- bad: badly—tad: **tadly**	
-10- beauty: beautician—Keauty: **keautician**	

Word Part Remover!—Section 2 -v2-	
Date: Student: Teacher:	
Skill Focus: Affix Deletion	**Correct = √**
Directions for Word Part Remover: Read the pseudo word for each item and wait for the student to give you the shortened version of the pseudo word which has had the affixes removed. The answer is in boldfaced type. Mark the correct responses with a check mark in the box on the right. Continue until the student has missed half or more of the test items on the page, then move to the next section.	
Practice: *"Repeat:* binking. *Remove the affix and say the shortened word."* (**bink**)	
-1- fets: **fet**	
-2- tanged: **tang**	
-3- mesting: **mest**	
-4- timly: **fim**	
-5- tarker: **tark**	
-6- felped: **felp**	
-7- runches: **runch**	
-8- pap: **papping**	
-9- bater: **bate**	
-10- bushion: **bush**	

Gluing Word Parts!—Section 3 -v2-	
Date: Student: Teacher:	
Skill Focus: Combining Word Parts	**Correct = √**
Directions for Gluing Word Parts: The evaluator will, slowly, say the parts of the word and the student will repeat the parts. The student then combines the parts to make a real word or pseudo word. The answers are in parentheses at the end of the item line. Mark the correct responses in the boxes, to the right. Stop when half or more of the items are missed, then move to the next section.	
Practice: "Repeat after me: 're' + 'do.' Combined it is **(redo)."**	
-1- "Repeat after me: 're' + 'tell.' Combined it is **(retell)."**	
-2- "Repeat after me: 'un' + 'equal.' Combined it is **(unequal)."**	
-3- "Repeat after me: 'in' + 'vent.' Combined it is **(invent)."**	
-4- "Repeat after me: 'dis' + 'honor.' Combined it is **(dishonor)."**	
-5- "Repeat after me: 'pre' + 'view.' Combined it is **(preview)."**	
-6"Repeat after me: 'mis' + 'pronounce.' Combined it is **(mispronounce)."**	
-7- "Repeat after me: 'try' + 'ing.' Combined it is **(trying)."**	
-8- "Repeat after me: 'care' + 'less.' Combined it is **(careless)."**	
-9- "Repeat after me: 'help' + 'ful.' Combined it is **(helpful)."**	
-10- "Repeat after me: 'in' + 'spect' + 'or.' Combined it is **(inspector)."**	

Finish the Sentence!—Section 4 -v2-	
Date: Student: Teacher:	
Skill Focus: Morpheme Pattern Match	Correct = √

Directions for Finish the Sentence: The evaluator will read the first two sentences, the first sentence of the next set, and then part of the next sentence, waiting for the student to complete it. The student should give you the answer that is in boldfaced type in the last sentence. Mark the correct responses in the boxes, to the right. Stop when half or more of the items are missed, then move to the next section.

Practice: "Listen to the first two sentences. Now listen again and see if you can finish the sentence when I stop. 'The jogger jogs: The speeder speeds.' 'The shopper shops: The singer ***sings.'"***

-1- He rest his head on the bench: He rests his head on the bench. The punishment fit the crime: The punishment **fits** the crime.	
-2- He walked on the path: He walks on the path. She cracked the egg: She **cracks** the egg.	
-3- The house is guarded: The house is unguarded. The car is protected: The car is **unprotected**.	
-4- The sweeper sweeps: The mopper mops. The stopper stops: The dipper **dips**.	
-5- The boy grabbed the bag from the shelf: The boy grabs the bag from the shelf. The dog begged for a bone: The dog **begs** for a bone.	
-6- Yesterday's homework was tricky: Today's homework is trickier. The blue box is heavy: The red box is **heavier**.	
-7- Don winks at Sandra: Don is winking at Sandra. Susie rents her car: Susie is **renting** her car.	
-8- Boston's snow is snowy: Bill's fish is fishy. The girl's slush is slushy: Her juice is **juicy**.	
-9- The fence is unnecessary: The fence is used unnecessarily. The game is unfair: The game is played **unfairly**.	
-10- Tom's room was in order: Kabir's room was in disorder. Olivia obeyed the rules: Angie **disobeyed** the rules.	

Word Play!—Section 5 -v2-	
Date: Student: Teacher:	
Skill Focus: Define Pseudo Words	Correct = √

Directions for Word Play: The evaluator will read the sentence containing pseudo words with real affixes. The student will tell what the sentence means by using the prefix meanings and offer a negative response. The answer is in bold at the end of the item. Mark the correct responses in the boxes, to the right. Stop when half or more of the items are missed, then move to the next section.

Practice: *"Listen as I read the sentence that has a made-up word and tell me what it means. 'The clown depainted his face, since he already had a big smile.'"* **(clown did not paint his face, because he had a big smile)**

-1- Felicia deliked the new furniture. **(Felicia did not like the new furniture)**	
-2- The robber disgrabbed the money bag. **(the robber did not grab the money bag)**	
-3- The boat defloated. **(the boat did not float)**	
-4- Darcy nonliked dancing. **(Darcy did not like dancing)**	
-5- Paula unwants to go shopping. **(Paula does not want to go shopping)**	
-6- The girl's rabbit unhopped under the bed. **(girl's rabbit did not hop under the bed)**	
-7- The pig disgobbled the food. **(the pig did not globble the food)**	
-8- Angie unhated the ice cream. **(Angie did not hate ice cream)**	
-9- Amanda's phone unrang with news of the baby. **(the phone did not ring with news about the baby)**	
-10- *The lady descreamed at the bug.* **(the lady did not scream at the bug)**	

Build the Word with Patterns!—Section 1 -v3-	
Date: Student: Teacher:	
Skill Focus: Affixation	Correct = √

Directions for Build the Word with Patterns: Slowly repeat the first two words, pause, then say the third word. Ask the student to supply the final word to complete the set. The answer is in bold for each item. Mark the correct response with a check mark in the box. Be sure to use the practice item first to help the student understand what is expected. Begin the test and continue until the student misses half or more of the items on the page, then move to the next section.

Practice: *"Listen:* gush: gushed. *Listen again:* tush. *What is next?"* **(tushed)**

-1- mock: mocked—bock: **bocked**	
-2- feel: feels—mol: **mols**	
-3- like: liking—wike: **wiking**	
-4- drop: dropper—frop: **fropper**	
-5- tick: ticker—fick: **ficker**	
-6- dots: dot—fots: **fot**	
-7- appear: disappear—comfort: **discomfort**	
-8- unkind: kind—unfit: **fit**	
-9- pure: purely—week: **weekly**	
-10- library: librarian—tibrary: **tibrarian**	

Word Part Remover!—Section 2 -v3-

Date: Student: Teacher:	
Skill Focus: Affix Deletion	**Correct = √**

Directions for Word Part Remover: Read the pseudo word for each item and wait for the student to give you the shortened version of the pseudo word which has had the affixes removed. The answer is in boldfaced type. Mark the correct responses with a check mark in the box on the right. Continue until the student has missed half or more of the test items on the page, then move to the next section.

Practice: *"Repeat:* binking. *Remove the affix and say the shortened word."* **(bink)**

-1- jids: **jid**	
-2- zanned: **zan**	
-3- gumping: **gump**	
-4- taintly: **taint**	
-5- ligger: **lig**	
-6- wumped: **wump**	
-7- fatches: **fatch**	
-8- fodding: **fod**	
-9- juder: **jude**	
-10- zortion: **zor**	

Gluing Word Parts!—Section 3 -v3-

Date: Student: Teacher:	
Skill Focus: Combining Word Parts	**Correct = √**

Directions for Gluing Word Parts: The evaluator will, slowly, say the parts of the word and the student will repeat the parts. The student then combines the parts to make a real word or pseudo word. The answers are in parentheses at the end of the item line. Mark the correct responses in the boxes, to the right. Stop when half or more of the items are missed, then move to the next section.

Practice: "Repeat after me: 're' + 'do.' Combined it is **(redo)."**

-1- "Repeat after me: 're' + 'view.' Combined it is **(review)."**	
-2- "Repeat after me: 'un' + 'load.' Combined it is **(unload)."**	
-3- "Repeat after me: 'in' + 'sensitive.' Combined it is **(insensitive)."**	
-4- "Repeat after me: 'dis' + 'allow.' Combined it is **(disallow)."**	
-5- "Repeat after me: 'pre' + 'cut.' Combined it is **(precut)."**	
-6- "Repeat after me: 'mis' + 'spell.' Combined it is **(misspell)."**	
-7- "Repeat after me: 'near' + 'ing.' Combined it is **(nearing)."**	
-8- "Repeat after me: 'heart' + 'less.' Combined it is **(heartless)."**	
-9- "Repeat after me: 'use' + 'ful.' Combined it is **(useful)."**	
-10- "Repeat after me: 'help' + 'ful' + 'ly.' Combined it is **(helpfully)."**	

Finish the Sentence!—Section 4 -v3-	
Date: Student: Teacher:	
Skill Focus: Morpheme Pattern Match	**Correct = √**

Directions for Finish the Sentence: The evaluator will read the first two sentences, the first sentence of the next set, and then part of the next sentence, waiting for the student to complete it. The student should give you the answer that is in boldfaced type in the last sentence. Mark the correct responses in the boxes, to the right. Stop when half or more of the items are missed, then move to the next section.

Practice: "Listen to the first two sentences. Now listen again and see if you can finish the sentence when I stop. 'The jogger jogs: The speeder speeds.' 'The shopper shops: The singer ***sings***.'"

-1- I drink water: She drinks water. I speak English: She **speaks** English.	
-2- Lisa brushed her hair: Lisa brushes her hair. Blake cooked the pasta: Blake **cooks** the pasta.	
-3- The magician's rabbit appeared: The magician's rabbit disappeared. The magician's rabbit zetted: The magician's rabbit **diszetted**.	
-4- The sleeper sleeps: The pinner pins. The guesser guesses: The spinner **spins**.	
-5- The officer cleared the parking lot: The officer clears the parking lot. The gardener trimmed the bushes: The gardener **trims** the bushes.	
-6- Meagan got up early: Shawn got up earlier. The necklace was shiny: The ring was **shinier**.	
-7- John fills the fish tank: John is filling the fish tank. Robert seals the hole: Robert is **sealing** the hole.	
-8- The grass is grassy: The brick is bricky. The breeze is breezy: The wind is **windy**.	
-9- The way she speaks is unflattering: She speaks unflatteringly. She is respectful. She acts very **respectfully**.	
-10- The assistant misprinted the form: The secretary printed the form. The children misbehaved for the babysitter: The children **behaved.**	

Word Play!—Section 5 -v3-	
Date: Student: Teacher:	
Skill Focus: Define Pseudo Words	**Correct = √**

Directions for Word Play: The evaluator will read the sentence containing pseudo words with real affixes. The student will tell what the sentence means by using the prefix meanings and offer a negative response. The answer is in bold at the end of the item. Mark the correct responses in the boxes, to the right. Stop when half or more of the items are missed, then move to the next section.

Practice: *"Listen as I read the sentence that has a made-up word and tell me what it means. 'The clown depainted his face, since he already had a big smile.'"* **(clown did not paint his face, because he had a big smile)**	
-1- Cynthia is unhating her new glasses. **(she does not hate her new glasses)**	
-2- The dog disbarked at the cat. **(the dog did not bark at the cat)**	
-3- Chase was happy, but he nonlaughed. **(he was happy, but he did not laugh)**	
-4- The hungry wolf was disafraid of the squirrel. **(the wolf was not afraid of the squirrel)**	
-5- The wasp unstung the boy. **(the wasp did not sting the boy)**	
-6- Robbie was desad with the new car. **(Robbie was not sad about the new car)**	
-7- The sun was shining, and it was unraining. **(the sun was out, and it was not raining)**	
-8- Going to the park in the rain was disfun. **(going to the park in the rain is no fun)**	
-9- The birthday cake was noneaten. **(the birthday cake was not eaten)**	
-10- The frogs were decroaking. **(the frogs were not croaking)**	

Build the Word with Patterns!—Section 1 -v4-	
Date: Student: Teacher:	
Skill Focus: Affixation	**Correct = √**

Directions for Build the Word with Patterns: Slowly repeat the first two words, pause, then say the third word. Ask the student to supply the final word to complete the set. The answer is in bold for each item. Mark the correct response with a check mark in the box. Be sure to use the practice item first to help the student understand what is expected. Begin the test and continue until the student misses half or more of the items on the page, then move to the next section.

Practice: **"***Listen:* gush: gushed. *Listen again:* tush. *What is next?*" **(tushed)**	
-1- fuse: fused huse: **hused**	
-2- fit: fits—ret: **rets**	
-3- fake: faking—hake: **haking**	
-4- flip: flipper—glip: **glipper**	
-5- crush: crusher—drush: **drusher**	
-6- cut: cuts—dut: **duts**	
-7- voluntary: involuntary—active: **inactive**	
-8- equal: unequal—polluted: **unpolluted**	
-9- second: secondly—third: **thirdly**	
-10- comedy: comedian—tomedy: **tomedian**	

Word Part Remover!—Section 2 -v4-	
Date: Student: Teacher:	
Skill Focus: Affix Deletion	Correct = √
Directions for Word Part Remover: Read the pseudo word for each item and wait for the student to give you the shortened version of the pseudo word which has had the affixes removed. The answer is in boldfaced type. Mark the correct responses with a check mark in the box on the right. Continue until the student has missed half or more of the test items on the page, then move to the next section.	
Practice: *"Repeat:* binking. *Remove the affix and say the shortened word."* **(bink)**	
-1- pabs: **pab**	
-2- binged: **bing**	
-3- jicking: **jick**	
-4- fadly: **fad**	
-5- teaker: **teak**	
-6- vished: **vish**	
-7- noxes: **nox**	
-8- kitting: **kit**	
-9- rafer: **rafe**	
-10- daption: **dap**	

Gluing Word Parts!—Section 3 -v4-	
Date: Student: Teacher:	
Skill Focus: Combining Word Parts	Correct = √
Directions for Gluing Word Parts: The evaluator will, slowly, say the parts of the word and the student will repeat the parts. The student then combines the parts to make a real word or pseudo word. The answers are in parentheses at the end of the item line. Mark the correct responses in the boxes, to the right. Stop when half or more of the items are missed, then move to the next section.	
Practice: "Repeat after me: 're' + 'do.' Combined it is **(redo)."**	
-1- "Repeat after me: 're' + 'load.' Combined it is **(reload)."**	
-2- "Repeat after me: 'un' + 'popular.' Combined it is **(unpopular)."**	
-3- "Repeat after me: 'in' + 'expensive.' Combined it is **(inexpensive)."**	
-4- "Repeat after me: 'dis' + 'pink.' Combined it is **(dispink)."**	
-5- "Repeat after me: 'pre' + 'dict.' Combined it is **(predict)."**	
-6- "Repeat after me: 'mis' + 'direct.' Combined it is **(misdirect)."**	
-7- "Repeat after me: 'mick' + 'ing.' Combined it is **(micking)."**	
-8- "Repeat after me: 'fear' + 'less.' Combined it is **(fearless)."**	
-9- "Repeat after me: 'care' + 'ful.' Combined it is **(careful)."**	
-10- "Repeat after me: 'un' + 'friend' + 'ly.' Combined it is **(unfriendly)."**	

Finish the Sentence!—Section 4 -v4-	
Date:　　　Student:　　　　　Teacher:	
Skill Focus: Morpheme Pattern Match	**Correct = √**

Directions for Finish the Sentence: The evaluator will read the first two sentences, the first sentence of the next set, and then part of the next sentence, waiting for the student to complete it. The student should give you the answer that is in boldfaced type in the last sentence. Mark the correct responses in the boxes, to the right. Stop when half or more of the items are missed, then move to the next section.	
Practice: "Listen to the first two sentences. Now listen again and see if you can finish the sentence when I stop. 'The jogger jogs: The speeder speeds.' 'The shopper shops: The singer ***sings***.'"	
-1- I rob wasps' nests: She robs wasps' nests. You lay the pillow down: She **lays** the pillow down.	
-2- The scouts hiked up the hill: The team hikes in the park. The scouts camped in the forest: The team **camps** at the park.	
-3- My birthday cake is iced: My birthday cake is reiced. Her pen was capped: Her pen was **recapped**.	
-4- The marker marks: The barker barks. The smeller smells: The cougher **coughs**.	
-5- It rained outside: It rains every afternoon. Robert closed the door: Chase usually **closes** the door.	
-6- Sidney's hair is silky: Carol's hair is silkier. Angela is busy: Katie is **busier**.	
-7- Betsy chills the soda: Betsy is chilling the soda. Tyler blends the ingredients for the pie: Tyler is **blending** the ingredients for the pie.	
-8- The curl on her head is curly: The grease is greasy. The gloss on her lips is glossy: The mist on the trees is **misty**.	
-9- The soldier is courageous: He is performing courageously. Bunny is affectionate: She is acting **affectionately**.	
-10- The lady was interested in buying the desk: The man was disinterested in buying the desk. Rosie was pleased with her work: Ellen was **displeased** with her work.	

Word Play!—Section 5 -v4-

Date:	Student:	Teacher:	
Skill Focus: Define Pseudo Words			**Correct = √**

Directions for Word Play: The evaluator will read the sentence containing pseudo words with real affixes. The student will tell what the sentence means by using the prefix meanings and offer a negative response. The answer is in bold at the end of the item. Mark the correct responses in the boxes, to the right. Stop when half or more of the items are missed, then move to the next section.

Practice: *"Listen as I read the sentence that has a made-up word and tell me what it means. 'The clown depainted his face, since he already had a big smile.'"* **(clown did not paint his face, because he had a big smile)**

-1- Children are disafraid of swinging. **(children are not afraid of swinging)**	
-2- Mice unwalked on the table. **(mice did not walk on the table)**	
-3- The mountain stream was decalm. **(the mountain stream was not calm)**	
-4- Carlita's brother unborrowed her car. **(her brother did not borrow her car)**	
-5- The family was safe after the car uncrashed. **(the car did not crash)**	
-6- Disrunning, the bandit left the bank with the money. **(the bandit did not run)**	
-7- The cows were unmooing. **(the cows did not moo)**	
-8- Marsha planned to untaste the cookies. **(Marsha did not taste the cookies)**	
-9- The magician's rabbit unappeared. **(the rabbit did not appear)**	
-10- The school bus disstopped for gas. **(the bus did not stop for gas)**	

Build the Word with Patterns!—Section 1 -v5-

Date:	Student:	Teacher:	
Skill Focus: Affixation			**Correct = √**

Directions for Build the Word with Patterns: Slowly repeat the first two words, pause, then say the third word. Ask the student to supply the final word to complete the set. The answer is in bold for each item. Mark the correct response with a check mark in the box. Be sure to use the practice item first to help the student understand what is expected. Begin the test and continue until the student misses half or more of the items on the page, then move to the next section.

Practice: *"Listen:* gush: gushed. *Listen again:* tush. *What is next?"* **(tushed)**

-1- smack: smacked—nack: **nacked**	
-2- fight: fights—bight: **bights**	
-3- lure: luring—mure: **muring**	
-4- lap: lapper—bap: **bapper**	
-5- flick: flicker—glick: **glicker**	
-6- fin: fins—zin: **zins**	
-7- own: disown—arm: **disarm**	
-8- believable: unbelievable—breakable: **unbreakable**	
-9- main: mainly—live: **lively**	
-10- guard: guardian—tuard: **tuardian**	

Word Part Remover!—Section 2 -v5-

Date:	Student:	Teacher:	

Skill Focus: Affix Deletion	Correct = √

Directions for Word Part Remover: Read the pseudo word for each item and wait for the student to give you the shortened version of the pseudo word which has had the affixes removed. The answer is in boldfaced type. Mark the correct responses with a check mark in the box on the right. Continue until the student has missed half or more of the test items on the page, then move to the next section.

Practice: *"Repeat:* binking. *Remove the affix and say the shortened word."* **(bink)**

-1- tofs: **tof**	
-2- dagged: **dag**	
-3- welping: **welp**	
-4- sartly: **sart**	
-5- flummer: **flum**	
-6- tropped: **trop**	
-7- lisses: **liss**	
-8- dopping: **dop**	
-9- marger: **marge**	
-10- tession: **tes**	

Gluing Word Parts!—Section 3 -v5-

Date:	Student:	Teacher:	

Skill Focus: Combining Word Parts	Correct = √

Directions for Gluing Word Parts: The evaluator will, slowly, say the parts of the word and the student will repeat the parts. The student then combines the parts to make a real word or pseudo word. The answers are in parentheses at the end of the item line. Mark the correct responses in the boxes, to the right. Stop when half or more of the items are missed, then move to the next section.

Practice: "Repeat after me: 're' + 'do.' Combined it is **(redo)."**

-1- "Repeat after me: 're' + 'seal.' Combined it is **(reseal)**."	
-2- "Repeat after me: 'un' + 'wise.' Combined it is **(unwise)**."	
-3- "Repeat after me: 'in' + 'yite.' Combined it is **(inyite)**."	
-4- "Repeat after me: 'dis' + 'miss.' Combined it is **(dismiss)**."	
-5- "Repeat after me: 'pre' + 'tize.' Combined it is **(pretize)**."	
-6- "Repeat after me: 'mis' + 'jight.' Combined it is **(misjight)**."	
-7- "Repeat after me: 'box' + 'ing.' Combined it is **(boxing)**."	
-8- "Repeat after me: 'rest' + 'less.' Combined it is **(restless)**."	
-9- "Repeat after me: 'thank' + 'ful.' Combined it is **(thankful)**."	
-10- "Repeat after me: 'un' + 'time' + 'ly.' Combined it is **(untimely)**."	

Finish the Sentence!—Section 4 -v5-	
Date: Student: Teacher:	
Skill Focus: Morpheme Pattern Match	**Correct = √**

Directions for Finish the Sentence: The evaluator will read the first two sentences, the first sentence of the next set, and then part of the next sentence, waiting for the student to complete it. The student should give you the answer that is in boldfaced type in the last sentence. Mark the correct responses in the boxes, to the right. Stop when half or more of the items are missed, then move to the next section.

Practice: "Listen to the first two sentences. Now listen again and see if you can finish the sentence when I stop. 'The jogger jogs: The speeder speeds.' 'The shopper shops: The singer ***sings***.'"

-1- Kevin fit the description: Kevin fits the description. Sonny spit the candy out: Sonny **spits** the candy out.	
-2- Sarah popped the balloon: Billy pops the balloon. The horse raced down the track: The horse **races** down the track.	
-3- Pigs rolled in the mud: Pigs unrolled in the mud. Horses taved in the barn: Horses **untaved** in the barn.	
-4- The rapper raps: The pincher pinches. The rider rides: The speaker **speaks**.	
-5- The boy closed the door: He closes the door every night. The team played baseball: The team **plays** baseball.	
-6- The chair is cozy: The sofa is cozier. Susan was hungry: Roy was **hungrier**.	
-7- George hunts deer: George is hunting deer. Rick stamps the ticket: Rick is **stamping** the ticket.	
-8- The ache is achy: The itch is itchy. The filth is filthy: The mess is **messy**.	
-9- Jim is delightful: Jim is acting delightfully. Jill's clothes are beautiful: Jill is dressed **beautifully**.	
-10- The vet located the dog: The vet mislocated the cat. The new rocket fired: The old rocket **misfired**.	

Word Play! — Section 5 -v5-

Date: Student: Teacher:	

Skill Focus: Define Pseudo Words	Correct = √

Directions for Word Play: The evaluator will read the sentence containing pseudo words with real affixes. The student will tell what the sentence means by using the prefix meanings and offer a negative response. The answer is in bold at the end of the item. Mark the correct responses in the boxes, to the right. Stop when half or more of the items are missed, then move to the next section.

Practice: *"Listen as I read the sentence that has a made-up word and tell me what it means. 'The clown depainted his face, since he already had a big smile.'"* **(clown did not paint his face, because he had a big smile)**

-1- Derinsing shampoo from your hair is bad. **(not rinsing shampoo is bad)**	
-2- The bear desmelled the honey. **(did not smell honey)**	
-3- The remote control unworked. **(the remote did not work)**	
-4- Cody diskicked the soccer ball. **(he did not kick the ball)**	
-5- It is better to deswallow gum. **(better not to swallow gum)**	
-6- Birds were untweeting in the garden. **(birds were not tweeting)**	
-7- Davis wanted to eat, but the waitress had distaken the order. **(the waitress did not take his order)**	
-8- The photographer desnapped her picture. **(did not snap her picture)**	
-9- Rex disbolted the door. **(he did not bolt the door)**	
-10- It is disfair to pick one winner. **(not fair to pick one winner)**	

Build the Word with Patterns! — Section 1 -v6-

Date: Student: Teacher:	

Skill Focus: Affixation	Correct = √

Directions for Build the Word with Patterns: Slowly repeat the first two words, pause, then say the third word. Ask the student to supply the final word to complete the set. The answer is in bold for each item. Mark the correct response with a check mark in the box. Be sure to use the practice item first to help the student understand what is expected. Begin the test and continue until the student misses half or more of the items on the page, then move to the next section.

Practice: *"Listen:* gush: gushed. *Listen again:* tush. *What is next?"* (**tushed**)

-1- free: freed— voo: **veed**	
-2- lake: lakes— dake: **dakes**	
-3- duke: duking— tuke: **tuking**	
-4- jog: jogger— tog: **togger**	
-5- rock: rocker— bock: **bocker**	
-6- bet: bets— ret: **rets**	
-7- respect: disrespect— allow: **disallow**	
-8- healthy: unhealthy— plugged: **unplugged**	
-9- slow: slowly— last: **lastly**	
-10- history: historian— fistory: **fistorian**	

Word Part Remover!—Section 2 -v6-

Date:	Student:	Teacher:	

Skill Focus: Affix Deletion	Correct = √

Directions for Word Part Remover: Read the pseudo word for each item and wait for the student to give you the shortened version of the pseudo word which has had the affixes removed. The answer is in boldfaced type. Mark the correct responses with a check mark in the box on the right. Continue until the student has missed half or more of the test items on the page, then move to the next section.

Practice: *"Repeat:* binking. *Remove the affix and say the shortened word."* (**bink**)

-1- luds: **lud**	
-2- pimmed: **pim**	
-3- mishing: **mish**	
-4- jearly: **jear**	
-5- tiner: **tine**	
-6- weached: **weach**	
-7- tuses: **tuse**	
-8- chetting: **chett**	
-9- larter: **lart**	
-10- dersion: **der**	

Gluing Word Parts!—Section 3 -v6-

Date:	Student:	Teacher:	

Skill Focus: Combining Word Parts	Correct = √

Directions for Gluing Word Parts: The evaluator will, slowly, say the parts of the word and the student will repeat the parts. The student then combines the parts to make a real word or pseudo word. The answers are in parentheses at the end of the item line. Mark the correct responses in the boxes, to the right. Stop when half or more of the items are missed, then move to the next section.

Practice: "Repeat after me: 're' + 'do.' Combined it is (redo)."

-1- "Repeat after me: 're' + 'order.' Combined it is (**reorder**)."	
-2- "Repeat after me: 'un' + 'usual.' Combined it is (**unusual**)."	
-3- "Repeat after me: 'in' + 'justice.' Combined it is (**injustice**)."	
-4- "Repeat after me: 'dis' + 'order.' Combined it is (**disorder**)."	
-5- "Repeat after me: 'pre' + 'pare.' Combined it is (**prepare**)."	
-6- "Repeat after me: 'mis' + 'happy.' Combined it is (**mishappy**)."	
-7- "Repeat after me: 'exit' + 'ing.' Combined it is (**exiting**)."	
-8- "Repeat after me: 'hope' + 'less.' Combined it is (**hopeless**)."	
-9- "Repeat after me: 'zat' + 'ful.' Combined it is (**zatful**)."	
-10- "Repeat after me: 'un' + 'think' + 'able.' Combined it is (**unthinkable**)."	

Finish the Sentence!—Section 4 -v6-	

Date:	Student:	Teacher:	

Skill Focus: Morpheme Pattern Match	Correct = √

Directions for Finish the Sentence: The evaluator will read the first two sentences, the first sentence of the next set, and then part of the next sentence, waiting for the student to complete it. The student should give you the answer that is in boldfaced type in the last sentence. Mark the correct responses in the boxes, to the right. Stop when half or more of the items are missed, then move to the next section.

Practice: "Listen to the first two sentences. Now listen again and see if you can finish the sentence when I stop. 'The jogger jogs: The speeder speeds.' 'The shopper shops: The singer ***sings.***'"

-1- Misty come to her senses: Misty comes to her senses. Sally push the button: Sally **pushes** the button.	
-2- She washed the dishes: She washes the dishes. He raked the leaves: He **rakes** the leaves.	
-3- Courtney asked her questions: Courtney reasked her questions. Frank clepped the clay: Frank **reclepped** the clay.	
-4- The caller calls: The kisser kisses. The banker banks: The shopper **shops**.	
-5- The boy pulled the cord: The girl pulls the cord. It snowed yesterday: It **snows** every day.	
-6- Erin is friendly: Elizabeth is friendlier. Justin's shoes were dirty: Joe's boots were **dirtier**.	
-7- The onion stinks: The onion is stinking. The burglar steals the money: The burglar is **stealing** the money.	
-8- The noise is noisy: The speed is speedy. The rain is rainy: The sun is **sunny**.	
-9- Tom is careless: Tom is acting carelessly. Debbie is disrespectful: Debbie is acting **disrespectfully**.	
-10- Nancy approved of the recipe: Nancy's grandfather disapproved of the recipe. Grandfather agreed with the weather report: Grandmother **disagreed** with the weather report.	

Word Play!—Section 5 -v6-

Date:	Student:	Teacher:	

Skill Focus: Define Pseudo Words	Correct = √

Directions for Word Play: The evaluator will read the sentence containing pseudo words with real affixes. The student will tell what the sentence means by using the prefix meanings and offer a negative response. The answer is in bold at the end of the item. Mark the correct responses in the boxes, to the right. Stop when half or more of the items are missed, then move to the next section.

Practice: *"Listen as I read the sentence that has a made-up word and tell me what it means. 'The clown depainted his face, since he already had a big smile.'"* **(clown did not paint his face, because he had a big smile)**

-1- The teacher said Ross was unbad. **(teacher said Ross was not bad)**	
-2- Skylar was dishappy with her mother. **(Skylar not happy with her mother)**	
-3- Dad uncalled Cody home. **(Dad did not call Cody home)**	
-4- Mary Elise diseats peanut butter. **(Mary Elise does not eat peanut butter)**	
-5- Beth unlooked at the TV. **(Beth did not look at the TV)**	
-6- Josh dekilled the snake. **(Josh did not kill the snake)**	
-7- The cat was deinterested in the mouse. **(cat was not interested in the mouse)**	
-8- Bo was unallowed to play with the ball. **(Bo was not allowed to play with ball)**	
-9- Jane was deloyal to her friends. **(Jane not loyal to her friends)**	
-10- Sonny is unpleased about the workload. **(Sonny not pleased about workload)**	

Build the Word with Patterns!—Section 1 -v7-

Date:	Student:	Teacher:	

Skill Focus: Affixation	Correct = √

Directions for Build the Word with Patterns: Slowly repeat the first two words, pause, then say the third word. Ask the student to supply the final word to complete the set. The answer is in bold for each item. Mark the correct response with a check mark in the box. Be sure to use the practice item first to help the student understand what is expected. Begin the test and continue until the student misses half or more of the items on the page, then move to the next section.

Practice: *"Listen:* gush: gushed. *Listen again:* tush. *What is next?"* **(tushed)**

-1- poke: poked—hoke: **hoked**	
-2- Beat: beats—zeat: **zeats**	
-3- move: moving—bove: **boving**	
-4- web: webber—meb: **mebber**	
-5- teach: teacher—meach: **meacher**	
-6- ten: tens—ren: **rens**	
-7- decision: indecision—coherent: **incoherent**	
-8- like: unlike—fasten: **unfasten**	
-9- honest: honestly—just: **justly**	
-10- politics: politician—molitics: **molitician**	

Word Part Remover!—Section 2 -v7-

Date: Student: Teacher:	

Skill Focus: Affix Deletion	Correct = √

Directions for Word Part Remover: Read the pseudo word for each item and wait for the student to give you the shortened version of the pseudo word which has had the affixes removed. The answer is in boldfaced type. Mark the correct responses with a check mark in the box on the right. Continue until the student has missed half or more of the test items on the page, then move to the next section.

Practice: *"Repeat:* binking. *Remove the affix and say the shortened word."* **(bink)**

-1- bems: **bem**	
-2- prabbed: **prab**	
-3- tanding: **tand**	
-4- murely: **mure**	
-5- plicker: **plick**	
-6- mipped: **mip**	
-7- jaxes: **jax**	
-8- zinning: **zin**	
-9- touder: **toud**	
-10- dormation: **dormat**	

Gluing Word Parts!—Section 3 -v7-

Date: Student: Teacher:	

Skill Focus: Combining Word Parts	Correct = √

Directions for Gluing Word Parts: The evaluator will, slowly, say the parts of the word and the student will repeat the parts. The student then combines the parts to make a real word or pseudo word. The answers are in parentheses at the end of the item line. Mark the correct responses in the boxes, to the right. Stop when half or more of the items are missed, then move to the next section.

Practice: "Repeat after me: 're' + 'do.' Combined it is **(redo)**."

-1- "Repeat after me: 're' + 'name.' Combined it is **(rename)**."	
-2- "Repeat after me: 'un' + 'necessary.' Combined it is **(unnecessary)**."	
-3- "Repeat after me: 'in' + 'put.' Combined it is **(input)**."	
-4- "Repeat after me: 'dis' + 'appear.' Combined it is **(disappear)**."	
-5- "Repeat after me: 'pre' + 'pay.' Combined it is **(prepay)**."	
-6- "Repeat after me: 'mis' + 'treat.' Combined it is **(mistreat)**."	
-7- "Repeat after me: 'dump' + 'ing.' Combined it is **(dumping)**."	
-8- "Repeat after me: 'thank' + 'less.' Combined it is **(thankless)**."	
-9- "Repeat after me: 'doubt' + 'ful.' Combined it is **(doubtful)**."	
-10- "Repeat after me: 'dis' + 'honor' + 'able.' Combined it is **(dishonorable)**."	

Finish the Sentence!—Section 4 -v7-

Date: Student: Teacher:	

Skill Focus: Morpheme Pattern Match	Correct = √

Directions for Finish the Sentence: The evaluator will read the first two sentences, the first sentence of the next set, and then part of the next sentence, waiting for the student to complete it. The student should give you the answer that is in boldfaced type in the last sentence. Mark the correct responses in the boxes, to the right. Stop when half or more of the items are missed, then move to the next section.

Practice: "Listen to the first two sentences. Now listen again and see if you can finish the sentence when I stop. 'The jogger jogs: The speeder speeds.' 'The shopper shops: The singer ***sings***.'"

-1- Richard set the book down: Richard sets the book down. Fran run the horse down: Fran **runs** the horse down.	
-2- The princess kissed the frog: She kisses many frogs. David missed many questions: Joel **misses** questions, too.	
-3- She tied her shoe: She untied her shoe. He mied his jacket: He **unmied** his jacket.	
-4- The tapper taps: The plugger plugs. The picker picks: The watcher **watches**.	
-5- Ben saved his money: Keri saves her money. Josh moved his truck: Josh moves his truck	
-6- The towel was handy: The wet wipes were handier. The worm felt slimy: The snail felt **slimier**.	
-7- Belinda looks at the birds: Belinda is looking at the birds. Tonya cleans her room: Tonya is **cleaning** her room.	
-8- The bat is batty: The fox is foxy. The dirt is dirty: The bush is **bushy**.	
-9- His conduct was in disorder: He was acting disorderly. The policeman was protective: The policeman acted **protectively**.	
-10- The girl understands the reason: The boy misunderstands the reason. The teacher managed the classroom: The substitute teacher **mismanaged** the classroom.	

Word Play!—Section 5 -v7-

Date: Student: Teacher:	

Skill Focus: Define Pseudo Words	Correct = √

Directions for Word Play: The evaluator will read the sentence containing pseudo words with real affixes. The student will tell what the sentence means by using the prefix meanings and offer a negative response. The answer is in bold at the end of the item. Mark the correct responses in the boxes, to the right. Stop when half or more of the items are missed, then move to the next section.

Practice: *"Listen as I read the sentence that has a made-up word and tell me what it means. 'The clown depainted his face, since he already had a big smile.'"* **(clown did not paint his face, because he had a big smile)**

-1- Julie is unhonest in her dealings. **(she is dishonest in dealings)**	
-2- The story is debelievable. **(the story is not believable)**	
-3- Prince Charming mistried the slipper on Cinderella's foot. **(did not try slipper on Cinderella)**	
-4- The case was deproven by the lawyer. **(the case was not proven by lawyer)**	
-5- The burning house was unviewed by Jeff. **(Jeff did not see the burning house)**	
-6- Wendy was deled down the wrong path. **(she was not led down the wrong path)**	
-7- The haunted house was unfeared by Frankie. **(she did not fear the haunted house)**	
-8- The gum was dechewed by the boy. **(he did not chew the gum)**	
-9- Tony's tools were dismoved. **(his tools were not moved)**	
-10- The man unmoved his finger from the button. **(he did not move his finger from the button)**	

Build the Word with Patterns!—Section 1 -v8-

Date: Student: Teacher:	

Skill Focus: Affixation	Correct = √

Directions for Build the Word with Patterns: Slowly repeat the first two words, pause, then say the third word. Ask the student to supply the final word to complete the set. The answer is in bold for each item. Mark the correct response with a check mark in the box. Be sure to use the practice item first to help the student understand what is expected. Begin the test and continue until the student misses half or more of the items on the page, then move to the next section.

Practice: *"Listen:* gush: gushed. *Listen again:* tush. *What is next?"* **(tushed)**

-1- fish: fished—mish: **mished**	
-2- mute: mutes—zute: **zutes**	
-3- face: facing—jace: **jacing**	
-4- rip: ripper—fip: **fipper**	
-5- lick: licker—mick: **micker**	
-6- lid: lids—fid: **fids**	
-7- agree: disagree—loyal: **disloyal**	
-8- popular: unpopular—polished: un**polished**	
-9- firm: firmly—love: **lovely**	
-10- mathematics: mathematician—bathematics: **bathematician**	

Word Part Remover!—Section 2 -v8-	
Date: Student: Teacher:	
Skill Focus: Affix Deletion	**Correct = √**
Directions for Word Part Remover: Read the pseudo word for each item and wait for the student to give you the shortened version of the pseudo word which has had the affixes removed. The answer is in boldfaced type. Mark the correct responses with a check mark in the box on the right. Continue until the student has missed half or more of the test items on the page, then move to the next section.	
Practice: *"Repeat:* binking. *Remove the affix and say the shortened word."* **(bink)**	
-1- yends: **yend**	
-2- natted: **nat**	
-3- tanging: **tang**	
-4- totly: **tot**	
-5- zighter: **zight**	
-6- tixed: **tix**	
-7- drashes: **drash**	
-8- magging: **mag**	
-9- jaster: **jast**	
-10- biction: **bic**	

Gluing Word Parts!—Section 3 -v8-	
Date: Student: Teacher:	
Skill Focus: Combining Word Parts	**Correct = √**
Directions for Gluing Word Parts: The evaluator will, slowly, say the parts of the word and the student will repeat the parts. The student then combines the parts to make a real word or pseudo word. The answers are in parentheses at the end of the item line. Mark the correct responses in the boxes, to the right. Stop when half or more of the items are missed, then move to the next section.	
Practice: "Repeat after me: 're' + 'do.' Combined it is **(redo)."**	
-1- "Repeat after me: 're' + 'count.' Combined it is **(recount)."**	
-2- "Repeat after me: 'un' + 'hurt.' Combined it is **(unhurt)."**	
-3- "Repeat after me: 'in' + 'frit.' Combined it is **(infrit)."**	
-4- "Repeat after me: 'dis' + 'fost.' Combined it is **(disfost)."**	
-5- "Repeat after me: 'pre' + 'school.' Combined it is **(preschool)."**	
-6- "Repeat after me: 'mis' + 'behave.' Combined it is **(misbehave)."**	
-7- "Repeat after me: 'mix' + 'ing.' Combined it is **(mixing)."**	
-8- "Repeat after me: 'sight' + 'less.' Combined it is **(sightless)."**	
-9- "Repeat after me: 'dread' + 'ful.' Combined it is **(dreadful)."**	
-10- "Repeat after me: 'mis' + 'jab' + 'ly.' Combined it is **(exporter)."**	

Finish the Sentence!—Section 4 -v8-

Date: Student: Teacher:	
Skill Focus: Morpheme Pattern Match	**Correct = √**

Directions for Finish the Sentence: The evaluator will read the first two sentences, the first sentence of the next set, and then part of the next sentence, waiting for the student to complete it. The student should give you the answer that is in boldfaced type in the last sentence. Mark the correct responses in the boxes, to the right. Stop when half or more of the items are missed, then move to the next section.

Practice: "Listen to the first two sentences. Now listen again and see if you can finish the sentence when I stop. 'The jogger jogs: The speeder speeds.' 'The shopper shops: The singer **sings**.'"

-1- Bill waked the bear: Bill wakes the bear. Judith popped the top on the soda: Judith **pops** the top on the soda	
-2- Rhonda mixed the cookie batter: Sue mixes cookie batter. Tim walked to the store: Sarah **walks** to the store.	
-3- Thomas filled the tank: Thomas refilled the tank. Ben zopped the tank: Ben **rezopped** the tank.	
-4- The blinker blinks: The slugger slugs. The tipper tips: The trapper **traps**.	
-5- He filled the water bottle: He fills the water bottle sometimes. He yelled at her: She **yells** at him.	
-6- The car was noisy: The train was noisier. Olivia's feet were smelly: Allen's feet were **smellier**.	
-7- The teacher talks to the children: The teacher is talking to the children. Brian jumps on the bed: Brian is **jumping** on the bed.	
-8- The milk is milky. The carrot is carroty: The caramel is caramelly: The bubble is **bubbly**.	
-9- Holly is incoherent: Holly is acting incoherently. Don is hopeless: Don is watching hopelessly.	
-10- Reed's telephone was connected: Paul's telephone was disconnected. The old food was infected: The new food was **disinfected**.	

Word Play!—Section 5 -v8-	
Date: Student: Teacher:	
Skill Focus: Define Pseudo Words	**Correct = √**

Directions for Word Play: The evaluator will read the sentence containing pseudo words with real affixes. The student will tell what the sentence means by using the prefix meanings and offer a negative response. The answer is in bold at the end of the item. Mark the correct responses in the boxes, to the right. Stop when half or more of the items are missed, then move to the next section.

Practice: *"Listen as I read the sentence that has a made-up word and tell me what it means. 'The clown depainted his face, since he already had a big smile.'"* **(clown did not paint his face, because he had a big smile)**

-1- Lana undrank the soda, because it was her sister's. **(did not drink soda because it was sister's)**	
-2- Don diswanted to stop at the store. **(he did not want to stop at the store)**	
-3- Zack could not play the song, because he depracticed his guitar. (**could not play song, because did not practice)**	
-4- The band director unlead the band, because he left the sheet music at home. **(did not lead band, no music)**	
-5- The doctor distreat the man's injury, because he was on vacation. **(did not treat man, because on vacation)**	
-6- Alex unswapped the toys. **(Alex did not swap the toys)**	
-7- It is no fun unswimming. **(no fun not swimming)**	
-8- They will unmake the cat eat the food. **(they will not make the cat he the food)**	
-9- Pam discried at the wedding, since it would make her eyes red. (did not cry at the wedding, since eyes would be red)	
-10- Emily's shoes were too large, because she untried them on. **(shoes too large, because did not try on)**	

Build the Word with Patterns!—Section 1 -v9-

Date:	Student:	Teacher:	

Skill Focus: Affixation	Correct = √

Directions for Build the Word with Patterns: Slowly repeat the first two words, pause, then say the third word. Ask the student to supply the final word to complete the set. The answer is in bold for each item. Mark the correct response with a check mark in the box. Be sure to use the practice item first to help the student understand what is expected. Begin the test and continue until the student misses half or more of the items on the page, then move to the next section.

Practice: *"Listen:* gush: gushed. *Listen again:* tush. *What is next?"* (**tushed**)

-1- fake: faked—jake: **jaked**	
-2- boat: boats—hoat: **hoats**	
-3- joke: joking— boke: **boking**	
-4- fat: fatter—gat: **gatter**	
-5- wreck: wrecker—freck: **frecker**	
-6- ban: bans—gan: **gans**	
-7- action: inaction—direct: **indirect**	
-8- fair: unfair—stable: un**stable**	
-9- bare: barely—fair: **fairly**	
-10- electric: electrician—clinic: **clinician**	

Word Part Remover!—Section 2 -v9-

Date:	Student:	Teacher:	

Skill Focus: Affix Deletion	Correct = √

Directions for Word Part Remover: Read the pseudo word for each item and wait for the student to give you the shortened version of the pseudo word which has had the affixes removed. The answer is in boldfaced type. Mark the correct responses with a check mark in the box on the right. Continue until the student has missed half or more of the test items on the page, then move to the next section.

Practice: *"Repeat:* binking. *Remove the affix and say the shortened word."* (**bink**)

-1- jants: **jant**	
-2- vanted: **vant**	
-3- haxing: **hax**	
-4- fostly: **fost**	
-5- frinner: **frin**	
-6- grepped: **grep**	
-7- plasses: **plass**	
-8- switting: **swit**	
-9- jaster: **jast**	
-10- dollection: **dollect**	

Gluing Word Parts!—Section 3 -v9-	
Date: Student: Teacher:	
Skill Focus: Combining Word Parts	**Correct = √**
Directions for Gluing Word Parts!: The evaluator will, slowly, say the parts of the word and the student will repeat the parts. The student then combines the parts to make a real word or pseudo word. The answers are in parentheses at the end of the item line. Mark the correct responses in the boxes, to the right. Stop when half or more of the items are missed, then move to the next section.	
Practice: "Repeat after me: 're' + 'do.' Combined it is **(redo).**"	
-1- "Repeat after me: 're' + 'take.' Combined it is **(retake).**"	
-2- "Repeat after me: 'un' + 'true.' Combined it is **(untrue).**"	
-3- "Repeat after me: 'in' + 'decision.' Combined it is **(indecision).**"	
-4- "Repeat after me: 'dis' + 'agree.' Combined it is **(disagree).**"	
-5- "Repeat after me: 'pre' + 'vent.' Combined it is **(prevent).**"	
-6- "Repeat after me: 'mis' + 'print.' Combined it is **(misprint).**"	
-7- "Repeat after me: 'read' + 'ing.' Combined it is **(reading).**"	
-8- "Repeat after me: 'jat' + 'less.' Combined it is **(jatless).**"	
-9- "Repeat after me: 'harm' + 'ful.' Combined it is **(harmful).**"	
-10- "Repeat after me: 're' + 'gain' + 's.' Combined it is **(regains).**"	

Finish the Sentence!—Section 4 -v9-	
Date: Student: Teacher:	
Skill Focus: Morpheme Pattern Match	Correct = √

Directions for Finish the Sentence: The evaluator will read the first two sentences, the first sentence of the next set, and then part of the next sentence, waiting for the student to complete it. The student should give you the answer that is in boldfaced type in the last sentence. Mark the correct responses in the boxes, to the right. Stop when half or more of the items are missed, then move to the next section.

Practice: "Listen to the first two sentences. Now listen again and see if you can finish the sentence when I stop. 'The jogger jogs: The speeder speeds.' 'The shopper shops: The singer ***sings.***'"

-1- The damp towel wet the bed: The damp towel wets the bed. Shelly rest her foot on the stool: Shelly **rests** her foot on the stool.	
-2- Reagan tapped the piano keys: Roger taps the keys sometimes. Fred jumped on the trampo-line: Mark **jumps** on the trampoline each day.	
-3- They earn equal pay: They earn unequal pay. The bat is able to hear the insect: The bat is **unable** to hear the insect.	
-4- The clipper clips: The carver carves. The wiper wipes: The sitter **sits**.	
-5- Ann loved her rabbit: Ann is loving her rabbit. Molly smiled at her friend: Molly **smiles** at her friend.	
-6- The dirt was gritty: The sand was grittier. Yesterday was foggy: Today is **foggier**.	
-7- Diane cracks eggs for breakfast: Diane is cracking eggs for breakfast. Doug breaks all the rules: Doug is **breaking** all the rules.	
-8- The beef is beefy: The taste is tasty. The grouch is grouchy: The boss is **bossy**.	
-9- Bob's behavior is predictive. Bob is behaving predicatively. Tim's behavior is shameful: Tim is acting **shamefully**.	
-10- The jury judged the younger boys: The jury misjudged the older boys. There was lots of trust in the room: There was some **mistrust** in the room.	

Word Play!—Section 5 -v9-	
Date: Student: Teacher:	
Skill Focus: Define Pseudo Words	**Correct = √**

Directions for Word Play: The evaluator will read the sentence containing pseudo words with real affixes. The student will tell what the sentence means by using the prefix meanings and offer a negative response. The answer is in bold at the end of the item. Mark the correct responses in the boxes, to the right. Stop when half or more of the items are missed, then move to the next section.

Practice: *"Listen as I read the sentence that has a made-up word and tell me what it means. 'The clown depainted his face, since he already had a big smile.'"* **(clown did not paint his face, because he had a big smile)**

-1- The two girls unskipped home, since it was hot. **(did not skip home, because too hot)**	
-2- Hayden untipped the waiter, because he was slow. **(did not tip waiter, because too slow)**	
-3- Stan dehammered the nail, because his elbow hurt. **(did not hammer nail, because hurt elbow)**	
-4- Meredith unscored the goal, because the time clock ran out. **(did not score goal, because time ran out)**	
-5- Cecil disdived in the pool, because it was shallow. **(did not dive in pool, too shallow)**	
-6- Jean unsmiled at her friend. **(did not smile at friend)**	
-7- The boy kept walking, because the snake dehissed. **(kept walking, because snake did not hiss)**	
-8- Lauren's fingernails were dispainted. **(fingernails were not painted)**	
-9- The car was streaky because Randy dewiped the wax off. **(car streaky, because wax was not wiped off)**	
-10- Riley unturned the key in the lock, because it was stuck. **(could not turn key, because stuck)**	

Build the Word with Patterns!—Section 1 -v10-

Date:	Student:	Teacher:	

Skill Focus: Affixation	Correct = √

Directions for Build the Word with Patterns: Slowly repeat the first two words, pause, then say the third word. Ask the student to supply the final word to complete the set. The answer is in bold for each item. Mark the correct response with a check mark in the box. Be sure to use the practice item first to help the student understand what is expected. Begin the test and continue until the student misses half or more of the items on the page, then move to the next section.

Practice: "*Listen:* gush: gushed. *Listen again:* tush. *What is next?*" **(tushed)**

-1- bake: baked—pake: **paked**	
-2- fat: fats—yat: **yats**	
-3- dice: dicing—fice: **ficing**	
-4- sip: sipper—vip: **vipper**	
-5- flush: flusher—dush: **dusher**	
-6- bed: beds—jed: **jeds**	
-7- order: disorder—engage: **disengage**	
-8- prepared: unprepared—changed: un**changed**	
-9- man: manly—open: **openly**	
-10- vegetable: vegetarian—simple: **simpletarian**	

Word Part Remover!—Section 2 -v10-

Date:	Student:	Teacher:	

Skill Focus: Affix Deletion	Correct = √

Directions for Word Part Remover: Read the pseudo word for each item and wait for the student to give you the shortened version of the pseudo word which has had the affixes removed. The answer is in boldfaced type. Mark the correct responses with a check mark in the box on the right. Continue until the student has missed half or more of the test items on the page, then move to the next section.

Practice: "*Repeat:* binking. *Remove the affix and say the shortened word.*" **(bink)**

-1- hakes: **hake**	
-2- fanded: **fand**	
-3- kitching: **kitch**	
-4- bicely: **bice**	
-5- fider: **fide**	
-6- doxed: **dox**	
-7- tweaches: **tweach**	
-8- pimming: **pim**	
-9- medder: **med**	
-10- sation: **sat**	

Gluing Word Parts!—Section 3 -v10-	
Date: Student: Teacher:	
Skill Focus: Combining Word Parts	**Correct = √**
Directions for Gluing Word Parts: The evaluator will, slowly, say the parts of the word and the student will repeat the parts. The student then combines the parts to make a real word or pseudo word. The answers are in parentheses at the end of the item line. Mark the correct responses in the boxes, to the right. Stop when half or more of the items are missed, then move to the next section.	
Practice: "Repeat after me: 're' + 'do.' Combined it is **(redo)."**	
-1- "Repeat after me: 're' + 'freeze.' Combined it is **(refreeze)."**	
-2- "Repeat after me: 'un' + 'lock.' Combined it is **(unlock)."**	
-3- "Repeat after me: 'in' + 'correct.' Combined it is **(incorrect)."**	
-4- "Repeat after me: 'dis' + 'jute.' Combined it is **(disjute)."**	
-5- "Repeat after me: 'pre' + 'set.' Combined it is **(preset)."**	
-6- "Repeat after me: 'mis' + 'read.' Combined it is **(misread)."**	
-7- "Repeat after me: 'vow' + 'ing.' Combined it is **(vowing)."**	
-8- "Repeat after me: 'speech' + 'less.' Combined it is **(speechless)."**	
-9- "Repeat after me: 'power' + 'ful.' Combined it is **(powerful)."**	
-10- "Repeat after me: 'un' + 'kind' + 'ly.' Combined it is **(unkindly)."**	

Finish the Sentence!—Section 4 -v10-

Date:	Student:	Teacher:	

Skill Focus: Morpheme Pattern Match	Correct = √

Directions for Finish the Sentence: The evaluator will read the first two sentences, the first sentence of the next set, and then part of the next sentence, waiting for the student to complete it. The student should give you the answer that is in boldfaced type in the last sentence. Mark the correct responses in the boxes, to the right. Stop when half or more of the items are missed, then move to the next section.

Practice: "Listen to the first two sentences. Now listen again and see if you can finish the sentence when I stop. 'The jogger jogs: The speeder speeds.' 'The shopper shops: The singer **sings**.'"

-1- Jack put the plug in the drain: Jack puts the plug in the drain. Vicky set the water on the table: Vicky **sets** the water on the table.	
-2- Robin packed her suitcase: Rod packs his suitcase. Bud looked in the box. Sam **looks** in the box.	
-3- Carmen loaded the computer program: Carmen reloaded the computer program. Rich booted the computer: Rich **rebooted** the computer.	
-4- The driver drives: The painter paints. The crafter crafts: The dreamer **dreams**.	
-5- Melissa named her pet pig: Melissa names all her pets. The boy climbed the tree: The girl **climbs the** tree.	
-6- During the picnic, the ants were pesky: During the picnic, the flies were peskier. The Brown Recluse spider is deadly: The Rattlesnake is **deadlier**.	
-7- The teacher marks the answers: The teacher is marking the answers. Connie misses her sister: Connie is **missing** her sister.	
-8- The mold is moldy: The stone is stony. The ants are antsy: The pigs are **piggy**.	
-9- The king is unbelievable: The king is acting unbelievably great. Walt's behavior is undesirable: Walt is acting **undesirably**.	
-10- The new worker was honest: The old worker was dishonest. The old worker was loyal: The new worker was **disloyal**.	

Word Play!—Section 5 -v10-	
Date: Student: Teacher:	
Skill Focus: Define Pseudo Words	**Correct = √**

Directions for Word Play: The evaluator will read the sentence containing pseudo words with real affixes. The student will tell what the sentence means by using the prefix meanings and offer a negative response. The answer is in bold at the end of the item. Mark the correct responses in the boxes, to the right. Stop when half or more of the items are missed, then move to the next section.

Practice: *"Listen as I read the sentence that has a made-up word and tell me what it means. 'The clown depainted his face, since he already had a big smile.'"* **(clown did not paint his face, because he had a big smile)**

-1- The newspaper was disdelivered, because delivery boy was sick. **(newspaper not delivered, because sick delivery boy)**	
-2- The pizza man unsliced the pizza, because the cutter was missing. **(pizza cutter missing, so did not slice pizza)**	
-3- Terry depacked the clothes. **(Terry did not pack the clothes)**	
-4- The fans discheered for the other team. **(fans did not cheer for other team)**	
-5- The boy unrode the horse, because his bridled was broken. **(boy did not ride horse, because broken bridle)**	
-6- My class dislearned fractions. **(my class did not learn fractions)**	
-7- Burt undrives the tractor. **(Burt does not drive the tractor)**	
-8- Ty desells many products. **(Ty does not sell many products)**	
-9- The car was disparked by Justin. **(car not parked by Justin)**	
-10- The t-shirt was undyed by Ty. **(Ty did not dye t-shirt)**	

||||||||||||||||||||||||||||||||||||||||||||||||||||||||||||||||||||||||||

TOOLBOX FOR TEACHING USING ASSESSMENT RESULTS

---

1   Toolbox items developed with Anna-Blair Hunt, MEd.

SOUND DISCRIMINATION TOOLS ||||||||||||||||||||||||||||||||||||||||||||||

PHONOLOGICAL—BIG UNITS OF SOUND

Rhyming with Simple Words

For this activity, plastic balls work best with smooth surfaces. Print pictures of the words, one word for each ball, from the word list with permanent marker. Ex: Card, Bay, Chime, Red, Sports, Boots, Ate, Cow, Dog, Mule, Fruits.

Explain to the students that this activity will involve listeners, speakers, and checkers. It is important that each group of people is paying attention to fulfill their role.

◊ The listeners will be the people sitting in the row, and when the ball is passed to that person, that listener has to hear the word that rhymes with the previous word printed on the ball.

◊ The speaker becomes the one person with the ball. This person's task is to make certain to move the ball to the next person as quickly as possible by saying a rhyming word with the printed word on the ball.

◊ The checkers will be the team of students who are not sitting in the row passing the ball. It is the task of that group to listen to assure that the rhyme has been complete, or to shout "negative" if the

word is not a rhyme. If the checkers are correct when yelling "negative," they will receive a point. If a negative is called and it is in fact a rhyme, the team that called the negative will then lose a point.

Materials
◊ Small plastic balls
◊ Black permanent marker
◊ Rhyming lists
◊ 1-minute timer

Have a team of five players sit a row. The first student will sit with their back to the second, the second will sit to their back to the third, and so on. The starting team member will select a printed word ball. This member will call the word and state a second word that rhymes. Once the rhyme has is called, the ball can be passed to the next person in the row. If a rhyme is incorrectly stated, the checkers can call "negative." Then that ball will be removed from the line and a new ball will be started at the first of the line.

Point values are as follows: 5 points for a ball being rhymed through all 5 members, 4 points for a ball making it through the line with 4 additional rhymes; and so on. Once the rhyme has been incorrectly stated, the ball is removed and no further points awarded. The time limit for 1 row's performance should be 1 minute.

Simple Sounds

For this activity, the students will accomplish Simple Sounds as a whole group. Using the following list, the teacher will create a set of 3 x 5 flash cards by printing a picture of each word on a separate card.

Word List

Giraffe	Cucumber	Dog
Bear	Penguin	Alligator
Engineer	Fish	Horse
Igloo	Jellyfish	Kangaroo
Lemon	Melon	Raccoon
Snail	Turtle	Umbrella
Violin	Wombat	Xylophone
Zebra		

Each student will be given a blank sheet of paper and instructed to number from 1 to 20. Once their papers are ready, the teacher will pair students into groups of two. The teacher will then explain that group member 1 will show a flash card, and group member 2 will say as many words with the initial sound until told to stop (1-minute timer). Group member 1 will count and record the number of correct initial sounds. Once students have gone through the deck once, the group members switch roles and do the flash cards again.

How to know you were a success?
The teacher will model the initial word and emphasize the starting sound.

EX: G—Giraffe

Materials
◊ Flashcards
◊ 1-minute timer

Word Count

For this activity, a familiar short interest level reading passage could be used. Short familiar riddles are good selections to help the student begin to anticipate the cadence.

Explain to the students that this activity will involve really good listeners. It is important that each person is paying attention to fulfill his or her role.

The teacher will explain to the students that they are to clap once for each word they hear. Appropriate cadence for the passage can assist those who have difficulty in understanding word recognition.

Materials

◊ Riddles
◊ Rhymes
◊ Should be familiar to the student

Sample sentences:

1. The dog barked loudly. (4)
2. Giraffes have very long necks. (5)
3. Cats chase mice. (3)
4. Do we go to school? (5)
5. The grass is green. (4)
6. Lions roar loudly. (3)
7. The thunder rumbled across the sky. (6)
8. Lunch is eaten at noon. (5)
9. The wheels turn on the bus. (6)
10. The man whistled. (3)

Teacher:

Everyone, please stand beside your chair. I will speak a sentence and afterward, you will clap the number of times words occur in the sentence.

Example:

The mouse ate cheese.

Students: Clap, clap, clap, clap

Teacher: How many times did you clap?
Students: 4.

Gluing Words Together

Within this activity, syllables will be identified and connections made to words with similar syllable breaks. The teacher will have the students sit in a circle. A beanbag or softball will be used to toss to the next participant.

How to know you were a success?

With each new picture displayed, the beanbag is tossed to a new student. This continues until all have participated.

Te le phone	Mac a ro ni
Al li ga tor	Cat er pil lar
Oc to pus	Dish wash er
Ham bur ger	Com pu ter

The teacher will begin by explaining that a word will be pronounced in syllables. It is helpful to have pictures of the words in a PowerPoint presentation with each word appearing individually. Explain that as a beanbag is tossed to an individual person, that person will immediately state the projected word in syllables. Then the student will say the whole word.

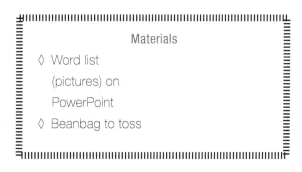

Materials
◊ Word list (pictures) on PowerPoint
◊ Beanbag to toss

Use Your Glue Again—Beginning Sound to Ending Sound!

Within this activity, the teacher will discuss that the onset is the initial unit of the word and the rime is the following letters of the word.

EX: d (onset) og (rime). EX: dog.

Materials

◊ Word list

(Paired students will listen to the teacher say a word. They will say the onset when the teacher points to the front of the bus and say the rime when the teacher points to the back of the bus. When both the onset and the rime have been said, Student A will practice pronouncing the onset and rime individually, and the partner, Student B, will blend the word. The roles then reverse for the next picture associated with a word.

Find the Sound!

Within this activity, teachers create flash cards (on 3 x 5 notecards) with pictures of different objects on each card. The flash card deck can be increased in multiples of 2 cards each representing an isolated beginning or ending sound.

It is important to label the picture with whether it is a beginning or an ending sound. Students will place each card facedown in rows and columns.

Once the cards are all facedown, Student A will turn over one card. Then the object is to find a second card with either the same beginning or ending sound. If the second card does not match, both cards will be returned to the facedown position. Student B then repeats the process, remembering the cards that have been shown.

How to know you were a success?

Once a pair of cards with a matching isolated sound has been found, that pair is 1 point for that player. The person with the most pairs wins the competition.

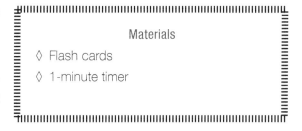

Materials
◊ Flash cards
◊ 1-minute timer

Find the Same Sound!

Within this activity, the teacher will instruct the students that they will identify the sound that is being represented in each set of words.

After citing the first word, a subsequent word will be said, and if a person guesses the sound that is being repeated, the student will get 3 points. If another word is given before a correct response is provided, the point value will decrease to 2 points. Again, if another word is provided before a correct answer is provided, the point value will decrease to 1 point. If a correct answer is not provided at this point, the teacher will provide the correct sound and no points will be awarded. The next set of words then will be completed.

Example Tally Sheet:

	3	2	1
Word 1			
Word 2			
Word 3			

Example:

◊ What is the sound that is the same as deck?
Dog, Desk, Dip (/d/)

◊ What is the sound that is the same as my?
Lie, Bye, Try (/i/ long i)

◊ What is the sound that is the same as mold?
Told, Fold, Scold (/o/ long o)

◊ What is the sound that is the same as red?
Bled, Mud, Sud (/d/)

◊ What is the sound that is the same as knack?
Knick, Nose, Knit (/n/)

Materials

◊ Dry-erase board
◊ Tally sheets for each student

Which Word Belongs!

Within the activity, the teacher will instruct the students to stand in a circle. Once students are in position, the teacher will explain they are doing a clapping game where they will categorize words that sound alike and different. The students will clap once when the words sound alike. When they hear a word that sounds different, they will clap three times fast. The first word will establish the sound that is to be targeted.

Example:

Cat, clap 1,   Hat, clap 1,   Mat, clap 1
Dog, clap three times fast.
(Ending Sounds)

Reset.

Cat, Clap 1, Keep, Clap 1, Certain, Clap
Three Times Fast
(Initial sounds)

Sample Lists:

1. Cat, Hat, Mat, Dog
2. Look, Book, Now
3. Pay, Say, Lay, Easy
4. Bunny, Funny, Worry
5. Dog, Fog, Log, Pig

How to know you were a success?

Once a word is stated that does not pair, the response will be a three-times clap. This will signify the word that does not belong.

Materials

◊ Sample lists
  • Initial
  • Ending

Word-Making Machine!

A great activity to have students begin by blending is by guessing the word with elaborated and lazy speech. To accomplish this activity, create a sock puppet with a plain sock complete with drawn eyes, mouth and nose. With Snoozy, the sock puppet, explain that Snoozy speaks a little differently because he is sleepy. Have the students guess the words that Snoozy is saying as he sounds the letters.

How to know you were a success?

Once the words are sounded individually and then blended, the student will receive a thumbs up from Snoozy.

Examples:

R___E_____D_____ (Red)
D___O____G_____(Dog)
C____A____T_____(Cat)
K___I_____T_____(Kit)
M___A_____P_____(Map)
P_____U_____G_____S (Pugs)
F_____A_____K_____R (Faker)
K_____A_____S_____T (Cast)

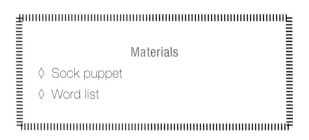

Materials
◊ Sock puppet
◊ Word list

Sound Count!

Within this activity, provide each student a string with a minimum of 5 beads on the string. Make sure that the string is long enough to have a clear separation of one end to the other. Also, make certain that both ending beads are unable to slip off by tying a knot in each end. When the students are sounding the word, they should move a bead for each new sound.

How to know you were a success?
Self-check can occur when the teacher demonstrates with her beaded string. Reset the beads after each word.

String of Bead Example:

```
‖‖‖‖‖‖‖‖‖‖‖‖‖‖‖‖‖‖‖‖‖‖‖‖‖‖‖‖‖‖‖‖‖‖‖‖‖‖‖‖‖‖‖‖‖‖
                        Materials
          ◊  String of 5 beads
‖‖‖‖‖‖‖‖‖‖‖‖‖‖‖‖‖‖‖‖‖‖‖‖‖‖‖‖‖‖‖‖‖‖‖‖‖‖‖‖‖‖‖‖‖‖
```

Remove the Sound!

Teacher: Notice there are some words within the following passage that are incomplete. Assist me in completing these omissions.

Example:

On Top Of . . .
On top of spaghetti all covered with cheese
I lost my poor meatball when somebody sneezed.

It rolled off the table, it rolled on the _oor,
and then my poor meatball rolled out of the _oor.

It rolled in the garden and under a _ush,
And then my poor meatball was nothing but _ush.

The mush was as tasty as tasty could _e,
And early next summer it grew to a _ee.

The tree was all covered with beautiful moss.
It grew great big meatballs and tomato sauce.

So if you eat spaghetti all covered with _eese,
Hold on to your meatball and don't ever _eeze.

Within this activity, the students will use manipulation to elevate their phonological awareness. To accomplish this, the teacher will provide lyrics with omissions.

How to know you were a success?
The students, as the rimes and cadence is established, will manipulate the words to develop the song.

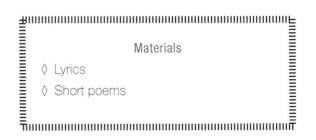

Materials
◊ Lyrics
◊ Short poems

WORD PART GAMES ||||||||||||||||||||||||||||||||||||||||||||||||||||||||||||||||||||||||||||||

MORPHOLOGICAL—WORD PARTS THAT CHANGE THE MEANING OF A WORD

Build the Word with Patterns!

Within this activity, the teacher will have the students stand in a circle around the room in pairs. A drum can be used to establish a musical beat to create a chant for the following song. The students will be instructed that they will respond to their partner's inserted word to form an analogy. A ball will be passed from one group to the next to establish order.

Teacher:

Ed makes an interesting change.

If rush became rushed, I say push, You say _____.

If please became pleased, I say work, You say _____.

When you say it like that, it all makes sense.

Ing makes an interesting change

If rush became rushing, I say work, You say _____.

If please became pleasing, I say push, You say

_____.

If run became running, I say give, You say _____.

When you say it like that, it all makes sense.

Er makes an interesting change

If rush became rusher, I say work, You say _____.

If please became pleaser, I say work, You say

_____.

If run became runner, I say give, You say _____.

When you say it like that, it all makes sense.

How to know you were a success?

Students will respond individually with the anticipated response.

+|||||||||||||||||||||||||||||||||||||||||||||||||||||||||||||||||||||||||
Materials
◊ Drum
◊ Soft ball
+|||||||||||||||||||||||||||||||||||||||||||||||||||||||||||||||||||||||||

Word Part Remover!

Within this activity, the teacher will need a large beach ball. On the ball, words, both pseudo words and real words with affixes, will be written with approximately four or five inches separating them. Students will form two lines facing each other. The first student will be handed the ball and where the left hand rests, the student will read the entire word. The student will then identify the base word.

Word list example:

1. scraped: **scrape**
2. grunted: **grunt**
3. worrying: **worry**
4. snaffer: **snaff**
5. dogs: **dog**
6. taking: **take**

How to know you were a success?

Once the correct response is given, the student will hand the beach ball to the person directly across from them. This will continue until all students have participated.

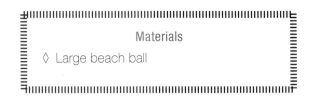

Materials

◊ Large beach ball

Gluing Word Parts!

Within this activity, the students, when paired with a partner will create multipmorphemic words. A 1-minute timer will be used.

The teacher will have in her hand a two morphemic start that she will hand to each partner as his or her turn occurs. With the class in a circle, students will be paired into Partner A and Partner B. One member of the partnership, Partner A, will state the prescribed beginning morphemes and the other member, Partner B will add the final morpheme.

Once the correct word has been formed, the ball will be passed to the next partnership.

Example:

Partner A: Unbeat; Partner B: Able

Unbreak	Cooperate
Maladjust	Predict
Uncomfort	Imperfect
Mistake	Expel

How to know you were a success?

The partnership with the ball when the timer sounds will be eliminated.

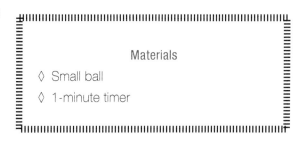

Materials
◊ Small ball
◊ 1-minute timer

Finish the Sentence!

Within this activity, the teacher would identify an easy reading selection where word endings are manipulated within the sentence. Have the students work in two groups. One person from each group will stand opposite of each other. The teacher will read the sentence, and she will instruct them to listen carefully as to how the words are being changed. The first person to state the correct word will score a point for their side.

Example:

The man struck the ball. The man strikes the ball. The ball bounced to the man. The ball _____ to the man. (bounces)

Example Sentences:

1. - The cat hit the dog: The cat hits the dog. The dog barked at the cat: The dog (**barks** —answer—) at the cat.
2. -The present is taped: The present is untaped. The suitcase is opened: The suitcase is (**unopened**).
3. He knocked on the screen: She knocks on the screen. She tossed the football: He (**tosses**) the football.
4. The hitter hits: The batter bats. The cleaner cleans: The sweeper (**sweeps**).
5. He panded the wall: He is panding the wall: He sinted the scale: He is (**sinting**) the scale.

How to know you were a success?
Self-check can occur when the teacher demonstrates with his or her beaded string. Reset the beads after each word.

Materials
◊ Sentence strips

6. She eats the broccoli: She stops eating the broccoli. The girl reads the book: The girl stops (reading) the book.
7. The mitter mits: The latter lats. The nailer nails: The runner (**runs**).
8. The girl likes to lean happerly: He is a good happer. The girl is a great linter: She can act very (**litingly**)
9. The dog daffed down his food: The dog is not daffing his water. The cat scorfed milk: The cat is not (**scorfing**) food.
10. The player unhooped the puck: The other player hooped the puck. The player unran the bat: The other player (**ran**) the bat.

Word Play!

Within this activity, groups of four students will use a list of prefixes and suffixes and create pseudo words to craft a story. In addition, the students will create a definition list of the words within the story. A minimum of eight new pseudo words must be included.

How to know you were a success?
Students will partner to identify their new words and to create definitions from those words.

Examples of:

Affixes to be used:
in, un, pre, able, ist, ing

Pseudo word roots to be used

gab, bik, dev, sig, nug, puf, w

Materials
◊ Prefix list
◊ Suffix list

REFERENCES

Fox, D. 2013. The Principal's Mind-Set for Data. *Leadership* 42 (3): 12–23.

Graney, S., & M. Shinn. 2005. The Effects of Reading Curriculum-Based Measurement (R-CBM) Teacher Feedback in General Education Classrooms. *School Psychology Review* 34: 184–201.

Guskey, T. R. 2003. How Classroom Assessments Can Improve Learning. *Educational Leadership* 5 (60): 2–18.

Moats, L. C. 2012. *Reconciling the Common Core Standards with Reading Research*. Perspectives on Language and Literacy. Washington, DC: American Federation of Teachers.

National Reading Panel. 2000. *Teaching Children to Read: An Evidence-Based Assessment of the Scientific Research Literature on Reading and Its Implications for Reading Instruction*. http://www.nichd.nih.gov/publications/nrp/smallbook.htm.

Overholt, R., & S. Szabocsik. 2013. Leadership Content Knowledge for Literacy: Connecting Literacy Teachers and Their Principals. *The Clearing House: A Journal of Educational Strategies, Issues and Ideas* 2: 86.

Popham, W. J. 1995. *Classroom Assessment: What Teachers Need to Know*. Needham Heights, MA: Allyn & Bacon.

Torgesen, J. K., & B. Bryant. 2004. *Test of Phonological Awareness, 2nd Edition: PLUS (TOPA-2+)*. Austin, TX: PRO-ED.

CPSIA information can be obtained
at www.ICGtesting.com
Printed in the USA
LVHW102327070920
665268LV00003B/5

9 781634 879835